A GIRL'S GUIDE TO FLY FISHING

A Girl's Guide to Fly Fishing

Reflex Fiction
Volume Three

REFLEX PRESS

First published as a collection in 2020 by Reflex Press
Abingdon, Oxfordshire, OX14 3SY
www.reflex.press

A CIP catalogue record of this book is
available from the British Library.

ISBN: 978-1-9161115-7-8

1 3 5 7 9 10 8 6 4 2

Printed and bound in Great Britain
by Clays Ltd, Elcograf S.p.A.

Cover image by LedyX/Shutterstock

www.reflex.press/a-girls-guide-to-fly-fishing/

CONTENTS

FOREWORD

This anthology brings the curtain down on another year of the Reflex flash fiction competition. And what a year it's been. 2019 saw the publication of the one-thousandth story on our website, the introduction of our choose-your-own-entry-fee policy, making our competition accessible to writers on low incomes, and to cap it all off, we were delighted to win the Saboteur Award for Best Anthology for last year's anthology, *The Real Jazz Baby: Reflex Fiction Volume Two*.

Since we started running this competition, one of our main objectives has been bringing flash fiction to a wider audience. That's why we showcase so many stories on our website. At the time of going to press, we've published over 1,150 stories by 750 different authors, each demonstrating a unique approach to the form. It is only through the generosity of those authors who allow us to publish their stories on our website, even when they've missed out on a prize, that we've been to achieve our objective.

Inside these pages you'll find 158 stories from 139 of the best flash fiction writers in the world, all longlisted for the four rounds of the Reflex flash fiction competition held in 2019. You'll find four winning stories: 'Cooped' by Andrew Stancek; 'The Puncture' by Lauren Collett; 'Intersection, Transit and Rose' by Gail Anderson; and the story that gives this anthology its name, 'A Girl's Guide to Fly Fishing' by Mary-Jane Holmes.

A Girl's Guide to Fly Fishing is the perfect introduction to readers new to flash fiction, and essential reading for those already familiar with what the form can offer.

We would like to thank our guest judges, Alison Moore, Claire Fuller, Naomi Booth, and Barbara Byar, and our team of volunteer readers coordinated by Katy Hill.

David Borrowdale
Editor, Reflex Press
June 2020

Cooped
Andrew Stancek

The car screeches in front of my house after running over my white rooster, Daniel.

The woman races out to the fluttering feathers and the bent comb. The man climbs out – squints at the jerking and the blood with the air of a man who'll never be surprised by a damn thing. The hens continue clucking and pecking inside their wire-fenced enclosure, unperturbed.

'She was driving too fast,' he says, 'but the bird shouldn't have been on the road.' I didn't clip Daniel's wings, didn't tether his leg. I don't explain.

Last Thanksgiving Day Paula turned to the wall, and her coughing stopped. Paula baked bread. Sourdough. Pumpkin seed. Chia. Dark rye. The house had paint peeling and shingles curling, but it breathed of warmth.

The woman has Daniel's blood on her hands when she gets up, a purple bruise on her cheek. She and the man are not matched. But no one ever is, I've found. Then one of you dies.

She nods when I offer a sandwich and a beer. They follow, and I cut thick slabs of bread, slather on mayo, slice turkey. He perches while she turns to the portrait of Paula gazing out the window at the birch. She steps to the window, recognizes the birch.

In the distance thunder rumbles, but it means little. False alarms, flashes of lightning.

I put out plates, three cans and we eat. He tells me where they are heading and why. He tells me the name of his company and the great opportunities for advancement. I nod. She has not looked at him since they stopped the car and hasn't said a word. When she strokes her purple bruise with a shiny red fingernail, he scrunches his beer can and throws it. The chicken clucks are clamorous.

He takes five twenties out of his wallet, fans them on the table. 'For the rooster and...' He pulls up his pants, adjusts his hat, strides to the porch, lets the screen door slam.

His car needs a muffler. She walks back to the picture of Paula and straightens it on the wall.

Big Strong Giant
Billy Cowan

I open the door and there he is. Sitting in my armchair with his linen cap on as if he belongs there, as if it's his home.

'I've got ten minutes, son,' he says. And all I can think of is Flash Gordon and his ten minutes to save the universe. Has he got ten minutes to save me? Is this why he's come back?

'I could make you some marmalade sandwiches and a cup a tay,' I say. 'That's doable.'

He smiles. I don't remember him ever smiling except in that one photograph taken on the fourteenth green after his hole-in-one, which I now keep secretly tucked into the back of a drawer, along with his linen cap.

'I have one memory,' he says. 'We're coming back from the Tonic and yer on my shoulders. Yer singing 'Everybody Wants to Be a Cat', and I'm holding onto yer ankles so you don't fall. Suddenly you stop singing and say, Da... you and me are like one big strong giant.'

I want to spit in his face, tell him about my memories, about the many terrible memories I keep – a wet towel dropped on a bedroom floor, a calloused hand squeezing my throat, a skelp that burns my skin red – but before I have a chance he speaks.

'And we were, son. Weren't we? One big strong giant?'

His eyes fill with water, and I realise he hasn't come back to save me, he wants me to save him. I hesitate. But then I feel his hands holding my ankles and hear a child's voice singing 'Everybody Wants to Be a Cat'.

I walk over to him, sit down on the arm of the chair. I take off his cap and kiss the top of his head.

Grease smears my lips.

Happicabs by Night
Izzy Paprika

Time passes weird in a cab office. It's separate from your own time. The car you send at 16:30 Tuesday and the car you send at 04:30 Wednesday make the same click of the mouse. You don't change in those twelve hours. All the hours are quiet. Still. They don't go slow, and they don't go quick either. It's not like a summer evening when the sun fades over the embers of a barbeque. Not like in the winter when you snuggle up to watch a series with your lover and then, before you know it, you're waking up in the middle of the night. The sun might rise and set, but that's outside. The lights stay always bright, cold, white. They keep you awake and confuse your body. Everything hums constantly. The server cabinet hums low, the monitor hums high, the extractor hums intermittently. When I hum, and I did used to hum, it doesn't sound like the sound is coming from me. Any noise in this office is as good as silence. Not the phone though.

That phone when it goes hits you like a bucket of ice. Sudden sharp and incessant I have heard it more times than you could ever begin to imagine. I wouldn't want you to try to imagine. It feels like a vacuum sucking up the stagnation for a second. You will hear it when you're on the toilet at home. It sometimes wakes you from your bed in the middle of the afternoon. You wonder why the person on the end of it is making their journey, but they don't think about you. Your life isn't happening here. Only the taxis and only the phone. But still, time passes weird. You have to remember how time really feels. You won't change in twelve hours, but you might in three years.

Blue Light

Adam Lock

Craig doesn't use his phone after eight o'clock because Marie fears blue light will interfere with their circadian rhythm.

It is dark in the kitchen. He opens the wicker box and takes out the phones.

Marie never changes her passcode.

He scrolls through her messages: the usual conversations with her mum, sister, friends. He reads the last conversation between himself and Marie.

Him: omw

Her: ?

Him: on my way

Her: bread, milk, batteries

He types on her phone and sends himself a message: need you to fuck me

He types on his own phone: how do you want it

Her: from behind – hard

The house is silent except for the ticking of the clock in the living room. He deletes the messages.

He pushes the charger into her phone; it resists, then clicks, and blue light illuminates the kitchen. He removes the charger then reattaches it. Male to female. He takes it out, and reattaches it, feeling for the point at which the connection yields and the screen lights up. He plugs in his phone, but the cable is split and no longer works.

The bedroom is cold. In bed, lying behind her, he kisses between her shoulder blades.

She mumbles something and moves away.

He reaches beneath his pillow for his phone. He googles how to repair a phone charger, but his phone won't connect to the internet. He tries again, but the battery dies, and the screen goes black.

Marie is a different person in the night – unreachable. There was a time he'd wake her, and they'd do it in the dead of night; she said it was like making love in a dream.

Unpunctuated Osmium

Jan Kaneen

strangers passing so close outside I can smell their fag smoke and diesel fumes too from the lorries raging past on the wet road that make the foundations shake and I can't believe I used to feel safe in here or take comfort from the outside being so close to the inside because there's only two flimsy inches of brick between me and it and a front door that opens out onto a thin pavement and if I could escape I would escape but I can't move because I'm made from the heaviest material known to humanity that I used to know the name of before I started changing and that I'd google now if I could only lift my fingers because when you left you said it was all bollocks and that the real truth is I'm a lazy bag of crap who should man-up and pull themselves together and think of someone else for a change like the starving millions who'd give their right eyes to have half of what I've got and I know you're right I know you're right I know your right but knowing it only makes me heavier still and I am telling the truth I really am telling the truth and I might not know the name of the heaviest substance known to humanity any more but things don't need to have a name for them to be real and you said it yourself that I'm like a huge black hole that drags you down exuding magnetic self-indulgence that seeps into everyone around me and that I never lift a finger to help myself or anyone else for that matter but that's because I can't lift a finger because I'm too heavy to move anything more substantial than air or the oxygen inside the air and I'm struggling really really struggling even with that

Effortless Circles

Michael Salander

My mum, always fascinated by Egyptology, lies like a pharaoh entombed in her hospital bed. She has hands of papyrus; no hieroglyphs or writing mark either fragile surface, but I can see her entire life written there. When I visit, her skeletal arms and hands have withdrawn from the world forever, lost beneath the sheets. An oscilloscope beeps by the bed. She says, 'Do *you* think I should go into a home?' It sounds brutal, but I just say, 'Yes'. I want to say, 'Of course not. I want you to be able to keep living in your own home' and then explain how in spite of that, I think a home would be a more practical and indeed necessary solution for her. But a bell is tolling, I am being ushered out; visiting time is over, along with so much more. Somewhere, punished by a merciless sun, archaeologists are scratching for bones buried beneath a cover of sand, a solitary vulture describing effortlessly terrifying circles in the azure sky above them. Outside, the dank December air punches the smell of disinfectant from my lungs, and the rain begins to fall. I, at least, am breathing. Along the street, an underdressed and overweight hen party are tottering drunkenly from pub to pub; each a dominatrix whose shoes refuse to obey them. Christmas is coming, and the fat are getting goosed. Beyond their shouting, the entirety of a life is being reduced to a single flat line on a screen.

Tastes like Salt

Alison Woodhouse

I want to be fluff, I say, the kind you blow off the head of a dandelion, pow.

Please be serious, you say. What do you want *really*?

I want superpowers like flying and disappearing and biffing the head off a giant robot who's threatening the planet's existence. I want to be a clean machine, sucking up the landfills, mashing up the metal in my cavernous insides and pouring out pure ozone. Actually, if I'm honest, all I want *really* is to float.

And why, you ask, in your literal, literally driving me mad, usual way, would you want to float?

Isn't it blindingly obvious, I don't say?

Because when the icebergs melt and the oceans rise and the land disappears only the floaters will survive, then the floating population will make towns and cities out of all the plastic that will rise to the surface of our landlessness and we'll have to learn to dive like South Sea pearlmen and the best of us will have lungs like iron and us floaters never cry, no we don't, and melting icebergs should taste like salt so why do they taste of nothing at all?

You've got that face on again that says you have no idea why we ever got married and you *really* want to talk about it but I'm not going to exhale, no I'm not.

The Pear

Julian Wakeling

The pear I was saving had gone rotten in my drawer so I couldn't eat it. I was disappointed at first, but this soon passed. It was only fit for the bin now, but I was loath to throw it away immediately. I felt a pause was only decent. This was a nonsensical sentimental gesture, but I couldn't help it. I took the pear out and placed it on the desk in front of me, and I was gazing at it with my face between my hands when my boss appeared. I didn't see her at first, but she acted as if that were her fault. She had a job for me and seemed nervous, as if she thought I might object. Yet behind the awkwardness I could sense her determination, and that made me feel sad, but whether this was for her or myself I couldn't say. She made a remark about the pear that was meant to be jocular but seemed forced. The job turned out to be very easy and the fears I'd had about it misplaced. The rest of the day passed painlessly enough. Colleagues came over occasionally to chat or ask me a question or to give me something small to do. I looked at the pear every now and then, admiring the colours and textures of putrefaction. I noted that it was starting to look like a potato. Some of the tasks I had to perform were very dull, but I rationalised that this is the price that most of us have to pay for the chance to dream. That made me feel better. Late in the afternoon it occurred to me that I had probably wasted my life.

Arigatou

Max Riddington

My dad is speaking Japanese. With a Leicester accent. He is not Japanese but was in Hiroshima during the war, after the bomb dropped, so he picked up a few phrases, none my mum ever wanted to hear. Back then he was eighteen and had hair. Small compensation for knowing every day you might die.

He's really dying now, he has the drugs and visitors on loop to prove it.

I am his only child and soon will be an orphan. Maybe I should get a cat. Maybe I am going mad.

'The closest I ever get to Japan is ordering sushi or watching that super tidy, tiny Netflix woman,' I say to dad. It's an instant conversation stopper.

I can't remember the last time dad and me had a proper chat, called each other on the phone to be the first with breaking news or just went for a walk and talked about the weather. Dad and Alzheimer's have been frenemies for years, sharing secret thoughts and shutting out the rest of us. Now Al has my dad talking Japanese. You've got to laugh. Till I cry.

Then I resume feeding dad some whizzed up pink gloop. He opens his mouth like a baby bird, the last in the nest to fledge. In between mouthfuls he says thank you over and over in a language I do not understand from a time I can never know. I repeat the words back, and in one incredible blink-and-you'll-miss-it moment, my father's blank eyes are re-born.

Arigatou, Al.

Orange Juice

J A Mason

We clean his house, the three of us. Only female branches left on this family tree now. Carbolic soap and water make urine-coloured nicotine rivulets run from the banisters to pool on the parquet.

In the kitchen: cartons and cartons of orange juice, unopened, bunched on counters and table-top, in plastic bags on the floor. Some, buffered by ultra-high temperature treatment, in date and almost appealing after the hot hours of scrubbing. Others look dangerously bloated, their convex sides distorting artists' impressions of dew-drizzled oranges. They all go into bin bags; what a waste. At least there's a neighbourhood-sized glass recycling bin out front.

'...to death,' Auntie finishes noting disapprovingly for the third time, as fuming dregs of several hues go down the sink in turn, a cocktail for the plumbing. I wonder what was wrong with the last fifths. Bit of a shame, we're all secretly thinking.

On the way home I stop at the supermarket on the corner, rewarding myself for not stinting on my labour in tribute to him even though none of us had seen him for months – years in my mum's case. Behind the counter: one-third off for Christmas (since Tuesday). I pick up a bottle of freshly-squeezed orange juice for appearances. They know me in there, after all.

The Irony

Julian Wakeling

I take the 7 train from Flushing to Manhattan to visit my mother, and I pass Citi Field baseball park and its parking lot, the site of Shea Stadium. When I arrive I mention it and ask her: didn't she once see the Beatles?

'August 15th 1965,' she says. 'I nearly fainted. The happiness was agony.'

I ask what they sounded like, but she says she has no idea: you couldn't hear them over the screams. When she puts down her cigarette and goes into the next room, I have to move the ashtray because the smoke is blowing in my face. She returns with a photo.

'Here. This was me at the Beatles concert.'

I see a sweet-looking kid with bangs and cat-eye glasses proudly wearing an 'I Love Ringo' button. I don't recognize her she's changed so much. When she picks up her cigarette, I remind her she has emphysema, but she just shrugs and replies:

'Life gets you one way or another.'

She takes the picture off me and looks at it fondly.

'It's ironic I should marry a man who looked nothing like Ringo.'

I don't say how pleased I am about that, or that I doubt it's really an irony. Then she tells me the story about the groundskeeper at Shea Stadium not letting the Beatles' road managers drive their small van across his precious turf, so they had to carry their equipment by hand.

'All that ground does now is hold cars,' I point out. 'That's an irony.'

Sitting quietly by the window in the raking light of the winter afternoon, cigarette in hand, she looks suddenly tired and old. And unimpressed.

'There's irony everywhere if you wait around long enough,' she sighs. 'It grows like weeds by the New Jersey Turnpike.'

Torch Song for a Thing That Never Happened
Andrew Leach

You read in the news about animals being slaughtered in Northern Europe because unprecedented drought meant a lack of hay to feed them. In Finland a record temperature of 34.3 degrees centigrade was recorded.

You recall the red hand mark across your mother's face in 1994 and the sound of your father slamming the front door. You can't remember what the weather was like, but you can remember that your ears felt hotter than the sun. You heard the sound of your father's Jaguar pulling away. Warming the tyres.

The UK has just recorded another hottest day. The Iberian Peninsula is anticipating temperatures of up to 50 degrees centigrade tomorrow. This is not normal, they say. Although it might be soon.

You remember smoking a cigarette on the morning of your wedding. You put it out on your wrist. Covered the burn with a Band-Aid.

Everything could have been different if only there'd been more warmth.

When love becomes comfortable it's hard to keep up the pretences. Campaigning for a better tomorrow loses its edge when you've forgotten how to feel today.

You still have the scar. You told someone it was caused by a gun. They said they didn't believe you in a way that suggested they might have.

Sometimes you create a scene so that you can bask in the frosty silence that follows. It's the only way to escape the unremitting heat.

If only they'd said I love you.

In Southern California a weatherman called Ryan says, 'It wasn't crazy hotter than it's ever been, but it was up there.'

You take a box of matches into the woods. You tell yourself you're just going out for a smoke. You just want to feel alive.

You think Ryan's an asshole.

You want to learn how to love her again. You just don't know where to begin.

Maybe the next one will be caused by a gun.

You stand and listen to the woodpecker. Urge him to fly.

The Trouble with Pirates

Tim Craig

'I'm a pirate,' he told her on their first date, touching his earring.

'The terror of the high seas.'

'How do I know that's true?' she asked.

'You don't,' he said and flashed her a smile. 'That's the trouble with pirates.'

That night, he came alongside to board her, and although she welcomed him with open arms, offering no resistance, still she went down with all hands, coming to rest on the soft bed.

She lay still and stared at the light filtering down from above, and, in time, made a home for coral, and kelp and starfish.

He couldn't stay, he said. Work to do on the Spanish Main. But before he went, with a stroke of the cutlass, he left behind his pirate's mark.

And buried a treasure deep in the warm sand of her body.

Nights were storm-tossed, mornings came in waves that left her ravaged and sick.

At the hospital, the sonographer mapped out the raised island of her belly and pointed at the screen with his pen.

'X marks the spot,' he said with a smile.

He captured an image in black and white: not much more than a skull and some bones: a spine curled like a seahorse.

'Do you want to know?' he asked.

'I already do,' she said.

She only took one copy and, at home, stuck it high on the door of the fridge

She looks at it every time she goes to get milk.

At the single, sunken eye, black like a patch. And the little fists clasping pearls in a watery grave.

Punctuation Marks in an Unknown Key
Matt Kendrick

Morning. Post-wake-up kiss. Stretch. Shower. Dress. Lingering gaze in your direction as I leave the bedroom. Downstairs, mechanically munching cornflakes. Brush, spit, toothpaste on collar. Frantic search for car keys which are neither in the bowl by the front door nor down the back of the sofa. Spare set. Ignition falters. Three attempts – fourth time's the charm. Close shave with the neighbour's wall, distracted by a glinting earring in the passenger footwell. Slantwise parking. Walking with heavy legs, cotton wool head. At work, the electric doors won't open; the lift confines me. Eyeballs stare on office entry. Computer juddering awake to fifteen hundred emails. Jenny who never does anything nice, for anyone, ever, offers me a cup of tea. Thanks. Don't mention it. Maureen makes dewy eyes from across the room. Boss asks, should you be here? I'm fine. Well, if you're sure. Then, tunnel vision engaged, scroll down for something easy. Something mechanical. Something safe. Words blur on trying to type. Backspace. Mental block over how to spell 'psychology'. Seventeen plus six won't add up inside my brain. So, resort to calculator. Resort to pretend typing to conjure the myth of productivity. Failing even at that. Motionless with fingers clutching wireless mouse. Two minutes. Screensaver launching. Pictures of an Andalusian holiday in springtime. Mountains, beach fronts, scenic villages. Us at a café drinking coffee, eating *bizcocho*. Your laughter. Your freckled cheeks. Your hair tickled by the wind. It triggers a subconscious response to be elsewhere. Wanting fresh air. Resorting instead to bathroom seclusion. Deep breaths in and out. Water splashed on face. Pretending it's hay fever when someone sees my reddened eyes. Boss suggests quick catch-up meeting. Sure. Five minutes? Yep. Short replies are just about manageable. Try to ignore his X-ray stare as he mentions possibilities. Phased return. Counselling. How about an after-work drink to take my mind off things? Really, all I want is sleep. Exhausted by the effort of it. Returning home to another condolence card on the doormat. In the bedroom, there's a smudge on the bedside photo frame from this morning's kiss. The photo of you on our wedding day.

Wind Turbine Army
Mark Newman

There is an army of wind turbines approaching, her father says, and they must be ready.

There are things her father is afraid of, things he warns her of, but she does not seem affected. She does not talk to strangers, has remembered to scream if they approach. She knows that children carry knives, but it is boys stabbing other boys – playground fights escalating – and does not involve her. She looks left and right when she crosses the road; she waits for the correct signals. She has an answer for all her father's fears.

The wind turbines are hard to ignore, she agrees. Sometimes the turbines stare straight at them, arms gently rotating – facing them down. Other times they look to the side, assessing some other victim in some other distance. Occasionally they turn to face each other, debating their next move. When they approach they multiply – overnight they send up replicas of themselves, long stringy poles standing to attention, peacocks strolling ever nearer, waiting for the command: wings unfold.

She imagines the sound if she could stand beneath them: something akin to a pylon's static hum.

There is an army of wind turbines approaching, her father says, and she finds herself mesmerised by their beauty. The languid way they move persuades her they mean no harm. Have you not heard of hypnotism, her father says, the way others can control your mind if you let them?

Let them come, she thinks. Let them come.

Out among the patio slabs, ants scurry, backs loaded. This is what we are to them, she thinks. When they come they will look down at us, barely a glance at the shapes we make. They will lift up their one leg, an ungainly hop, and leap over us, indifferent.

Stopping Distance

Gabrielle Turner

It will happen, I promise you. At least once in your life. It changes you forever. It tastes like metal when you brake, and the sound? Somebody shouting. Sirens, coming to take you away.

I know what most people would do. It's human instinct. But me, I close my eyes, and I go faster, faster, till I fly.

It starts in the kitchen, with the kind of cramp that makes you gasp. I lie on my back, stretch out on the cold slate, and the relief is divine. Then, I see it. You find all sorts, under the cabinets. Crumbs, of course. A bamboo skewer. A black hairpin, the splayed-out kind that holds French twists together. The kind of hair I'll never have.

I'm looking at somebody else's story, written on the kitchen floor. It ruptures me. I give it a week. We hardly speak. You don't notice. It wakes me up, the thought of a new life. In the mornings my shoulders ache like I've been flying all night.

The best way to escape bad weather is to fly away. This is called migration, and many millions of birds do it every year.

What's the opposite of flying? Perhaps I'm a dodo. I'm a doll strapped into this metal robot, and we're too heavy to take off. It's your fault.

I'm looking ahead. The freeway. Where does it end? How long?

When migrating, the birds who are not strong enough simply fall out of the sky.

I found the crumbs, John, I tell you at sixty, seventy, eighty. *The hairpin. That's what gave it away.*

A voice is shouting beside me: *slow down, Carla, stop.*

I should brake. The line goes dead. I taste metal. Somewhere, there are sirens.

Haar: Fog Rolling In from the Sea
Clare Weze

When I was an in-between age – not really old but not that young –
I took a fisherman's cottage in the northeast, complete with wood-
burning stove, lime-washed walls and a new word for fog. The town
was full of artists. We threw pots, painted landscapes and egged
each other's politics on like starlings gathered across wires.

Nobody knew what to do when the minke whale beached itself;
those who might have known were long gone. There was a haar that
day, and of course, somebody captured it in watercolour, another on
film, but the whale stayed beached. I flapped; others dictated; nothing worked.

By the time the RNLI volunteers arrived, we were falling out and
in a state of extreme faff. But taking instruction, we formed a team
and got the whale back to sea. I kept the blowhole clear of water, and
as the whale and I made eye contact, an accordion-player gave us
something Celtic-sounding and a cheer went up. People brought out
bottles of pale ale, as if they'd planned everything.

That night I joined the whale in a dream. We set out into a black
sea, and he explained his worldview over deep ocean trenches, beneath stars. He told me things my dreaming brain couldn't even
comprehend, much less invent. He assumed I was familiar with
magnetic north and wanted to know why humans don't take advantage of the Gulf Stream. Why do we put to sea at all when our nav-
igation systems are flat and haphazard, and we flail in the water?
I tried to explain, apologising for my species along the way, but he
said there was no need. He'd lost his family too; I understood that
well enough.

The air was sweet with something like whisky and sponge pudding, and savoury with lobster breath. On the last stretch, he sang
me a song of the hunger that seizes your guts after the hundredth
unlucky mile. The middle eight spoke of the hypnotic whoosh when
your lover breaches, and I woke in tangled sheets with grit between
my toes and a briny tongue.

Hidden House
Patrick Flanary

'Of course,' he grumbled as he flushed the toilet a second time. *She's such a Jessica.* He inspected his nostrils in the mirror. Back at the bar Jessica applied more lipstick, the severe crimson staining the rim of her glass.

When he offered up his Manhattan cherry, she didn't hesitate. Things had started out promising: pints of Yanjing over Peking duck and green beans. Jessica had remarked on his proficiency with chopsticks, and he liked that. But when the first-date talk veered toward the topic of marriage, he'd hollered for the check.

He knew the perfect diversion, an unmarked pub nearby with only two stools. 'Why don't you pick up the phone,' he'd nodded toward a wall draped in artificial ivy.

Lifting the handset triggered a sliding panel that revealed an expanse of *Gatsby*-era décor: sulking cummerbunds, worn leather-bound couches, a gramophone crackling with jazz. It all made the acrid funk of cigar smoke tolerable. Still, he wondered: Why did Jessica want to meet just before taking that headhunter job in Shanghai?

'I leave Beijing after New Year's Eve,' she'd texted. No punctuation, but an emoji stifling its own giddiness with one hand. Maybe Jessica wanted a fling. Yes, maybe tonight, with no tomorrows in store, they would beat the holiday intrusion of solitude together.

He was exhausted by expectation. Outside, restraint failed him.

'My roommate's in Norway for Christmas,' he said into his upturned collar. A lonely tuk-tuk rattled by. He winced at hearing himself repeat the invitation, jingled the change in his pocket. 'No,' Jessica said and pulled her hair under a reindeer cap. 'One more drink. Then I'm off to pack boxes.'

Such a Brady, she thought, as they stepped into slicing wind. Or was it Bradley? Jessica couldn't remember. She'd already put the city behind her.

Exquisite Metamorphosis

Yasmin Al-Jarrah

It stops raining and the sun comes out. I hang my skin out to dry among stringy lines of sheets and onesies. The warm sirocco feels good as I'm lifted up, flapping and ballooning in the air.

My mind goes back to the day I first became aware of my skin, when he forced himself on me, leaving me sore, frightened and angry. Blotches and blisters developed, following the patterns of my nerves, spreading across my epidermis. They formed scabs that peeled and dropped off.

I grew to like the protection provided by the increasing threads of my scars. I became a seducer of men who could inflict more wounds and developed a thick network of fierce, fibrous tissue. My skin shed regularly leaving filigree lace pockets behind, revealing, new, glossy, black, brown and white patterned scales.

I became a snake in an urban forest. My long, vibrating forked tongue learned to feel and scent, while my body grew strong for squeezing and my extendable jaws stretched to accommodate many sizes.

I became proficient in slowly swallowing my prey, inch by inch, gulp by gulp. I started with water rats, voles and moles, progressing to foxes and eventually, to men wishing to harm me. The digestion period took several weeks, depending on the size of the mammal.

They say I am cold-blooded, but this is only partially true. My blood is warmed as the sun penetrates through my protective layer to my veins. When not hunting, I rest, conserving energy; staying camouflaged by lying in lacunae, muted hue rock.

My skin is dry now, so I zip myself back into it.

Moving stealthily, cautiously, I scent you lying among daisies and long grass. You reach out to me and gently stroke my scales. Without fear, I coil under your armpit and sleep by your side.

Stuffed

Paul Croucher

Lolly was my first friend. She had a bone-white body with a cherry-red face, and she lived in a wrinkled plastic jacket, buried beneath my pillow. My treat, if the scales allowed, used to be five licks of her sticky head. But only on the first of each month, and only after my star jumps.

'A fad' was how Dad described it. As if parmesan skin and alopecia were akin to a boy band obsession. In his quest for a fix, he'd clamp my nose like a vice. Stuffing down foreign objects in-between my gasps, and pinching harder as my mouth pinballed them away, tumbling down my front like boulders off a cliff.

He removed the toilet lock, with mustard eyes, in two swings. Therefore, on gas mark five went my Dulcolax brownies. They tasted like blackboard dust and not even *his* Old Spice could submerge the effects. He found them eventually, obviously. And then it was his fingers, those bitten Castrol-rimmed nails raking my oesophagus, that forced their way inside and kept digging, cramming.

At my appointment, I made him take the stairs. My chewing gum bones throbbed all the way, but it was worth it. To see him sweat, to see him pant. On my terms. There, Mum turned the magazines over, failing to recognise the protagonist as ever, and dressed like a chef, the doctor produced a plate of acronyms, ramming them down my throat.

All eyes except Dad's (Super Sunday apparently) watched my first session. In the hope a meatball would break the seal. I heaved it towards me and stared as the reformulated beef leaked tears of built-up, ingrained sludge. Their eyes widened. But my Minnie Mouse gown ceded an ankle, a hippo ankle, an elephant with DVT, and their ballpoints clicked back into hiding.

I sat with Mum in the Cafe. Opposite, a girl jigged in her seat as if weightless. She licked her finger, dabbed for crumbs, and confessed in a gazillion reasons her love for Princess Sofia. For every word, she exchanged scone. It appeared, from here, that for something to go in, something first had to come out.

I Want to Die but I Have Things to Do

Melanie Czerwinski

I eye the Kansai *dashi shoyu* chips from a distance. I hear a little tune play from the overhead speakers as someone else enters the convenience store. The aisles are tight, tight enough that when I'm not alone in them, I have to twist my fat American hips so I don't bump into the other customers. It smells like Family Mart fried chicken but in a good way. My stomach gurgles.

My sweat-slicked hand picks up the foil bag, crinkles it, leaves a trail of slime like a nervous slug. We ate these chips in your one-room Leopalace apartment before you vanished. It was Tuesday. You had gone to the bar with your coworkers after your shift was over, making me wait in the cold and the snow and the dark at your door. My hair was damp with snow that melted as soon as it hit the heat of my scalp.

You eventually stumbled my way, bundled to the nose in a thick scarf, the tips of your ears blood-swollen in your intoxication. Before you fished your keys out of your pockets, you pursed your lips around a Hi-Lite.

'I want to die,' you told me, lighting the cigarette between your fat lips, 'but I have things to do.'

That was the last night I saw you. Now I'm alone with a stranger in Family Mart, looking at snacks to distract me from those words you left me with. The potato mascot on the bag raises his finger at me, opens his mouth in a small *O*, doesn't make eye contact with me. I always had a soft spot for women like you, who kissed me with the taste of *shoyu* on their tongues and had a death wish.

I bring the chips to the cashier who slurs *hyakujuunanaen*. The yen sticks to my sweaty palm as I try to drop it in the tray, the same way I was stuck to you, in some slimy, sticky membrane. As I head for the door, I wonder what things you have to do that are more important than I was to you.

For the first time, I want to live.

The Disintegration of Silks

Mary Thompson

Sofia's smoke spirals out across the river, all faint and fuzzy in the burnished evening light. How she longs to follow its trail and disappear into nothingness like a gentle ghost. In the distance she notices a sailing boat, gliding steadily towards the sea. How she wishes she were on it, gazing into the mystical brume.

In the corner of the freshly cleaned room, she spots a spider's web, spun without her realising. Her husband will wonder why it's still there. Savouring this quiet act of rebellion, she watches the minuscule arachnid inching its way around its new creation, infusing life into its sterile surroundings.

Sofia moves into the remaining patch of sun and stares over the balcony. People are streaming back and forth across Vauxhall Bridge. She observes the cyclists, joggers, and frazzled commuters. How she longs to escape, if only through sleep, but her nights remain dreamless, soulless affairs.

I'm a bird in a gilded cage, she whispers in her thick Russian accent, regurgitating a phrase from her English Book of Idioms. And as she hears the click of the door, she blows on the web as though it were a dandelion clock and watches as the silks disintegrate.

A Life in Numbers

Chris Wright

Jim rubbed his hands together and blew into them like he was trying to start a fire. Sarah's hands remained limp on her lap, unaffected by the sporadic glances he made as if to will her to feel the cold and do something about it.

'Aren't you cold?'

'What?'

'I'm sure your fingers are freezing.'

He reached over, but her hands fell between her leg and the chair.

'Suit yourself.'

A flutter of snow rested against her skirt before turning transparent and vanishing altogether.

'It's wrong.'

'What?'

'The day. We wouldn't have made it today.'

'I thought you said you came every day.'

She raised her head, eyes locked on a leaf, stiff and rattling along the tarmac path that cut through the brown felt banks of the park.

'How could you let him say those things? Standing there, beside him.'

'I told him what I could, and he filled in the blanks.'

'I couldn't watch. This man I don't know telling me what I do. Summing up a life in milestones, in numbers.'

'He probably does it with everyone.'

'Tell me then, what number's love? What equation's bond? What figure can tell the story of a whole life relative to another?'

'I've no idea.'

Sarah wriggled like a child getting a haircut. Jim glared at the trees until the criss-crossed branches drew macabre faces on the used cotton wool sky. 'It's too cold to snow,' he would have said had it not already been snowing.

Sleepless Nights

Lisa Fransson

I stuff her body with glass microbeads wrapped in strips of shredded baby-vests, organic cotton-soft to the touch, until she rests solid in my arms. I finish her seams with a blanket stitch in newborn pink, and I inject life into her lips with blood-red stem stitches. Then I define her features with French knot-nostrils, a pale brown to give the illusion of depth. But her eyes I light with aquamarine stem stitches around dark pupils that give her a gaze so ancient that I can hardly suffer to meet it. Her scalp I leave bare as I find nothing soft enough to emulate the feathery feel of that first baby hair.

I dress her in a tiny baby grow from the pack on the shelf under the changing station and sing quietly to her as I place her in the Moses basket. Now I hear him stir on the other side of the wall, calling my name and I know that it must be late.

As I crouch down to rock her to sleep, my belly flops onto my thighs. I rest my chin on my arm. 'Mummy's here,' I whisper. But those eyes hold me fast, and I think how I must fashion eyelids that can close, at least sometimes. Meanwhile, I lift her up again and hold her head next to my heart-beat, bouncing her gently, hushing her, and when I bend down to kiss her, her cheek is soaked with my milk.

Dreamcatchers

Julie Evans

Early rays glint on the two dreamcatchers that hang from the ceiling on silk threads. Isla, so excited when I had said, 'Guess what, Sis!' sent them from America, from the Grey Bear Reservation. Certificates of their authenticity are framed on the walls, each so beautiful, stamped with the handprints of the maker, Maemaengwahn ('a butterfly'). The whorls of her fingertips on the paper, over-emphasised in the dark dye, paint a wild Van Gogh sky, spirals blurring into tentacles. I thought her magic would protect them.

The room is daydream white. Rachel, forever nervous, said it was a 'safe' colour, though the dreamcatchers have pigment in the tiny orange tesserae, the blue glass beads and pale feathers – gender non-specific, though I had allocated them in my mind. The two discs swirl clockwise together in perfect synchronicity, fanned by the breeze from the crack-open window, winnowing motes of summer dust.

The voice reciting in my head is Isla's, her reassurance, though she knows, truthfully, how it is. She is, after all, my own twin. All through the shadowy night, I have been trying to adapt to the new reality, to fit consoling thoughts of gratitude into boxes in my brain, but instead, I have swallowed them. They are stuck somewhere deep, clinging to the bumpy walls of my intestine, impaled on protruding villi.

I pull the blue dreamcatcher towards me and snap the fragile thread. The other remains, spinning alone now, silently feminine. The circle of bent willow fits exactly inside the palm of my hand, my broken Boy's-Own dreams held fast in the spider web of sinew string. Together in the sharp morning light, the dreamcatcher and I, severed and inert, stare at the bars of the left-hand cot, wondering how to begin the disassembly.

Mammy Bongs
Eleanor Talbot

The shot was vigorous. That's what a tearful Onke told the policeman when he asked. It was how Mammy Bongs described the water on her first-ever visit to the seaside in 2001.

'Onkgopotse, see how vigorous the ocean is. It's as if it thinks of itself as the only thing on earth.'

Gunshots were like that – a split second of nothing else.

The sand burnt their feet on the dash to the waves. It was funny when Mammy leapt, her fat boomerang legs conked at the knees, her huge breasts bounding like happy dogs. The best was her face, eyes smiley slits, mouth open so wide you could count all her teeth.

The policeman wrote *vigoris* in his notebook, scratched it out, this time *vigaris*.

'Haai man, this vigorous thing. Was it close or far?'

Mammy Bongs is only a memory, and now there's nothing but trouble. Problems with men, money and work. If only she were here to deliver her favourite lecture: 'Choose a man with your head, not your hot places and work hard, save up.'

Onke glanced at the gun parcelled in a clear forensic bag and wished she hadn't spent her retrenchment on Sokks's bail and a sexy nightie. Sokks was bad in the beginning and bad at the end. In the middle, he'd sometimes been soft and close, but those moments were rare, replaced by a fast temper and hard knuckles.

'One shot. From inside. I was pegging washing.'

The policeman looked up at her. She'd done her best to wrap a scarf around her head to hide the hurt underneath.

'He had a case open. Armed Robbery.'

Onke nodded.

'And you found him like that?'

The mound under the sheet was tidy, as if he'd carefully laid down and died. Surrounded by piles of money, it was an ominous shrine.

'Strange no cash taken,' said the policeman, pen poised.

'Maybe there was more,' said Onke, feeling practised tears well up and slip down her cheeks.

There'd been much more. Onke thought of Mammy on the shoreline and resolved to be as vigorous as the water, for once, the only thing on earth.

On the Way Home

Stephen Palmer

As the train passes over a viaduct, I see a man standing in a field taking a photograph of a train as it passes over a viaduct.

The man is surprised by a sudden mist descending as it does in these parts. When, after a while, it is warmed away by the sun, the train has gone but so too, much to the man's unease, has the viaduct.

He looks down at the playback on the camera. There is the train passing over the viaduct and behind it the grey sky, the green fields divided by drystone walls and the sheep, both black and white; the grey of the narrow tarmac road meandering from behind a hill down into the valley. A subdued landscape but subtle and shifting. The sunlight, when it does manage to break through the layers of cloud, tends to be watery but still changes the tone and texture of what lies beneath.

As it does now as the man looks around. The landscape has changed. All that remains is the grey sky above and below stretches of greenery bounded by the horizon. Like the viaduct, the sheep have gone. There is, though, some trace left of what the future will bring. A path, unplanned but well-trodden as it meanders from behind a hill down into the valley, tells of where the narrow tarmac road will one day be.

A woman is walking along this path. There are no buildings or farmsteads or villages in sight and nothing to suggest where the path leads or the woman is going. The man raises his camera and photographs her.

The mist descends again and then rises. Grey drystone walls beneath a grey sky. Black and white sheep. The grey of the narrow tarmac road meandering its way from behind a hill down into the valley. The man looks down at the playback on his camera. There is nothing there but a blank, grey square. The man climbs up on to the tarmac road and begins to follow in the path of the woman's long erased footsteps as the train carries me on to my destination.

A Careless Smile
Lee Hamblin

The barber arranges his tools on the countertop, turns the pot of tonic so the whirly logo shows. He's handsome, like a young Dirk Bogarde. He sings along to a recycled song busting out from wall speakers, a song I'm old enough to remember the tipsy-soaked original, and this gets me thinking of Patti, who loved that song, or maybe it's the soft-lit mirror I'm gazing into, just as we did one summer in sultry Seville when posturing naked together in front of a huge baroque dresser, her saying that nobody ever sees you the way you see yourself, not the real you, the you that matters. All I saw was she looking beautiful, me with my careless smile. I didn't get what she was talking about until a long time after.

The last time I saw Patti…

I arrive at her apartment finding the door slightly ajar; so I nudge it open, take a peek inside. Standing stone still in front of the window, she's framed in skyscraper neon, wearing the ancient cat-picked woollen sweater I hate: washed-out black and shapeless. *Cozy*, she always called it. Or was it *comfy*?

'You seen the time?' I say, tapping my wrist, knowing we're late already. The spooky silence of no reply hangs in the air, rhythmically interrupted by a static click coming from the turntable, the picture-sleeve of *that* song strewn on the floor. There's a pair of kitchen scissors in her right hand, and when her left arm reaches up and grabs a hunk of hair, I notice the hole in her sleeve where her elbow pokes through. The woollen thread straddled across the grainy, pinked flesh looks like a last-ditch attempt of a bald man trying not to be, which makes me snigger, and makes her hack away at the chestnut bouquet she's gripping. Her eyes don't waver or water. I'm struck dumb. She throws the cutting at my feet, repeats, and all the while that stupid cat of hers sits perched on the sofa's armrest, watching like he understands all that I don't, being more a man than I'll ever be.

Coming Home

Nancy Hogg

Today was a good day. They dropped a bomb on the house. I woke to hear the sky shaking. I lay in my sleeping bag, still as a broken bird. The wall of our dream house has been blown off. The yellow wallpaper, you never liked, is flapping in the breeze. My world is ash. But when I close my eyes, everything is bright.

It is not the cold ending I imagined. It is a soft, hot whisper. It is your proximity. I am returning to you. I am returning to us.

I can see the silver birch tree in our garden, its bark blazing softly in the light from the kitchen. I am smoking a cigarette out of the bedroom window, watching as the cold air swells the billowing smoke. 'I'm waiting,' you call out from the bed.

I see our bodies moving in the half-light. I recognise the blue duvet cover your sister bought us when we moved in; crushed by our feet at the bottom of the bed and stained with a pattern of blurring moons. I'll wash it tomorrow. Probably.

The floor of the kitchen is warm beneath my feet. I hear water bubbling, the soft bump of potatoes on the stove; the wet 'kish' as you open a can of lager. I like this kitchen more than I remember. The mosaic of cracked tiles, the cutlery drawer that sticks; I wouldn't change a thing. You've walked mud across the floor again, but I don't care. To clean a house is to make a new beginning. Ours for the taking. Your hair is as black as the day I met you.

'How was your day?' you ask me, absentmindedly.

I take the can of lager from your hand and take a long glorious drink.

'It was good, they dropped a bomb on the house,' I say, 'what's for tea?'

As Hallowed As the Earth

Alyssa Jordan

Sometime after the funeral, you started drinking from the glass that held her flowers.

Your hands, clumsy with grief, shook a little as they upended the tall glass over the sink. Flowers with tender petals spilled out carelessly. Inside, clumps of leaves and gritty nutrients stuck to the glass. You didn't wash it first. Instead, you filled it with water and greedily drank. When that wasn't enough, you refilled it again, and again, until you were gasping for more.

Your husband watched silently from the kitchen table. His mouth had pressed into a thin white line.

You didn't know how to explain any of this to him. In the past you would have tried, but now things were too surreal, too knife-edged. Your swollen fingers tightened around the glass with a claw-like grip.

At first, the water had tasted like dirt and earth, like mildew and that musky smell of nature that was somehow welcome yet unpleasant. After so many refills, all that remained was the faint tang of metal.

You drank from it still.

A few days passed before the glass briefly disappeared. Your husband returned it freshly washed between the tips of his fingers. Pure, sparkling water filled it to the brim.

You went outside and sank your nails into the dirt, broke the even ground with quick, angry jabs, until you produced clumpy handfuls of earth and packed as much as you could into the glass.

It trembled under the constant strain. You reminded yourself to gentle your touch; glass was fragile, and something easily broken.

No more things would break, you thought, ignoring the dirt that pillowed on your thighs and stained your knees.

When you drank the last mouthful of muddy water, you held on to the taste as long as you could, tried to make it a part of you before it could vanish as if it was never there, as if it hadn't already taken the very air from your lungs.

Half of you had been unmade in the earth.

You only wanted to reclaim it.

Pretend Play Pretend Living
Jennifer Riddalls

They arrived in the night, just as dark snuck in and blew out the last of the sun. Headlights swooped around in the darkness like toppled lighthouses. We leaned out of our window listening to the cars revving in the mud, filling the space where nothing should be. We sneaked onto the stairs, all hush-hush, being eary-wigs. Weird words floated up. 'Dirty spongers' we heard Da say. I turned to Luke.

'If dirty people have sponges, why aren't they clean?' I asked.

Luke snorted a laugh so hard that snot flew out. We quick-crawled bug-like to our room, laughed with the duvets stuffed into our mouths till our tummies hurt and the laughing tears dried up sad.

Now it's morning, and Ma is quiet. She always is on mornings. Luke says she's had too many again. No one ever tells me what of. Da looks outside, face like a bad smell. We run to the bottom of the garden, ignore Da banging on the glass and squish our faces against the kite-shaped wire between us and the field. All over, caravans have appeared like crooked teeth in grassy gums. A boy comes near, and his football tings the wire.

Luke clambers over then pulls me after. The long grass nips at my ankles, dogs run with us, chase the ball. Luke stops to talk to a girl who's put all her hair on top of her head in a big heap. An old man leans from his door, offers me strips of bacon. The salt pops on my tongue and out pops a question I've been holding in like breath.

'Why do you live on holiday?'

The man smiles, his face crinkly like scrunched up paper.

'Why not?' He says and laughs from his belly up.

I laugh too. It sounds like pretend play, pretend living. Luke tags me to run again. Da is at the fence now, our half-house like a prison behind him. 'Boys,' he warns, loud-whispering at us when we pass. We pretend not to hear him, hiding giggles. Later, I cry when the caravans start leaving, forced away, leaving muddy holes where life should be.

Fatal Flaw

Louise Mangos

You open your eyes, and there is a perfectly formed snowflake sitting on the glove in front of your face. You can't move your limbs. You've lost your goggles, and you're unsure which way is up. Your ears are packed with snow, and the silence is a tinnitus roar in your head.

As your breath labours through lack of oxygen, you recall the stuffiness of the bar, the smell of stale beer and overheated bodies. You remember bragging about your achievements on the slopes, each of you claiming a longer, steeper descent, beer bottles clinking louder with each round.

The thorns of a multitude of tiny crystals linked like soldiers in the stormy night, creating a vast army of white. In the blizzard, they assembled and swelled, curling themselves into a cornice.

The dawn air was as honed as a glass bayonet. In the calm of morning, the troops waited for the first wisp of wind to tip their balance. As the rising sun glittered on the slope, your skis teetered on the lip of the wave, anticipating the joy of the sweeping fall. You jumped, and a serpentine furrow appeared behind you, refilling with a feathery layer. You pushed on, sucked down by temptation. Your single victory cry echoed in the gulley.

And the snow released its hold on the mountain to chase you in silent menace.

Now your eyes burn with cold, as tears try to form. No one knows you're here. The others were too hungover to take up the challenge. It was you and nature, making a pact, and now your cheeks are brushed with her kiss of betrayal.

In your fading coffin you concentrate on the absolute perfection of that microscopic crystal with six fragile arms sprouting delicate spikes. You know this thing of beauty has an infinitesimal speck at its nucleus, a nanoparticle of dust around which water condensed in the troposphere, before freezing into a unique miracle and falling to the mountain.

A solitary accomplishment only possible because of one fatal flaw.

Cat's Cradle

Jessica Douthwaite

Tina peered at me with cymophanous eyes. Face hooded by brows as buckled as the stretcher. Not even on first name terms; I, too, was bundled into the ambulance at the school gates.

The night before, fourteen-year-old Tina watched TV, giggling forgetfully. Her mum scowled, 'sad cow,' then, 'stupid bitch.' Tina's skin sagged. Her ribs itched. Last time she visited the doctor 'death' felt comfortable like a rain-washed ditch. 'She will die,' he cautioned a social worker, 'her asthma is caustic.' The nicotine-stained cats padding around her mum's flat were 'sparks to kindling' inflected the Doctor. It was a school night, but Tina thought about fire instead of sleeping, holding her breath on the sitting room sofa. Her lungs howled, lonely but for lingering cigarette smog. A braying cough galloped away in the night. 'Shut up,' shouted her mum from her bedroom, where cats snuffed and snored.

In the morning, Tina careened into school; a confusion of unwashed uniform, shocked hair, and schoolbag full of unsolicited scorn. Hers was an escapees' gait – rocking on ankles ready to break. She knew about 'death'. Another girl paraded a pencil case steeped in foul colours like marshmallow pink and lavender lilac. Tina, sleep-shrunken and shallow, growled, 'sad cow.' She ignited a torrent of scratching and jeering; her peers discordantly amused. The fight drew blood. Tina – retrieved by the Principal – sang 'stupid bitch' on their way to the office. Her swallowed breath quietened corridors as they moved further away.

The asthma grabbed her throat from inside; scooped out her ribs; tightly peeled away the air on her lips. I held her while she mewed, spewed and scratched at the paramedics who loaded her into the ambulance. She fizzed away. We were not even on first name terms. 'Sir,' she expired.

Older Brother
Mahesh Nair

We arrive at Path Labs where chairs fill the round hall like spikes on a virus. My Elisa report is at the front desk. You say, *You'll never get moksha*. I say, *I love rebirths*. I hand the report to you and leave.

You'd disliked my choices, but I was unbound like unstrung beads. And Sofia was naked in a tiny room. A beedi between her fingers and her legs apart. *Bring it*, she moaned.

You had mentioned condom and trafficking, but she said, *I'm clean and I enjoy this*.

And it was the best sex, and we met a few times. My innate disposition to attain a transcendent state, however brief. Your celibacy for moksha from the cycle of birth and death – a sham.

Weeks later, a burning sensation lingered after I used the restroom, lymph nodes swelled on my neck, chills seized me, and Google confirmed I'd die a painful death.

From Path Labs, I head to Old Bazaar where the red-light district pulses with people on road, machines on sidewalk, utility poles above. Cows cuddling, men flashing, and pimps chasing. The cacophony of their infectious frenzy. And you know by now if I'm infected – or perhaps not, preferring first to drape your rudraksha between your middle and index fingers, using your thumb to count the beads, reciting your chant.

I enter a building, walk up five floors of dingy stairway – into a packed hall where incense sticks burn, soliciting is intimate, and beedis between fingers. Around the hall are several pine doors for the tiny rooms, where men exploit the weak, obeying karmic impulses. When I ask for Sofia, a pimp leads me to a balcony, and says, *She died*.

I jump too, hoping that a head-first fall would give me instant death and rebirth, but my head's stuck in a V-shaped pole. The street below is unresponsive, like your beads in a ceaseless chant.

Sirens.

The dogged tang of a hospital bed. A familiar voice. The gradual clarity of you waving Elisa, rudraksha around your neck. You take a rudraksha out of your pocket, wrap it around my report, and grin.

Stone Heart

Jim Toal

Thirty years on, the lustreless grey stone in my studio still gleams in my imagination. A sea jewel slipped cold and wet into my pocket for safe-keeping as we leave the beach on our honeymoon. Quickly forgotten.

A life transforming materials borne by the tide: bone, wood, rope, stone. This, a last reliquary of love.

The saw blade slices it in two, each half warm in my hard palm. A grinding disk hollows a bowl in both cut surfaces. Finer brushes polish them smooth. In each facing edge, I chisel a recess to conceal a hinge and drill four fine screw holes. The hinge secured, the halves closed together; the join is seamless, the stone perfect. I drill another hole for the eyelet.

I decant my blood into a spherical glass phial. There was no protest at the haematology clinic to my request, only a raised eyebrow before the nurse drew the murky port from my vein into the syringe. To prevent curdling, the phial bobs in a cup of cold water while I burn off the vacuum bulb with a blowtorch. When complete, it is a deep ruby, a candlelit bauble.

The phial sits in the hollow of the stone snug as a nut in its shell. I thread the silver chain through the eyelet and put the stone and chain inside a small box lined with down. Slide the box into a jiffy-bag, ready to post.

To arrive on the morning of our anniversary, when you'll tear the seal and prise open the box. Lifted from its nest of tiny feathers, you'll assess its weight on your fingertips. Feel its coolness against your throat. Despite worrying its smooth surface, forever you'll remain unaware of the join, forever oblivious of the way to its still, dark heart.

The Cereal Cafe

Abi Hennig

It arrived from nowhere: fully grown, an explosion of colour, an animated cuddle squeezed between the betting shop and a boarded-up wreck that had once been a cinema but now served only as a slur on the name of nostalgia and a home to multiple generations of rats. The locals looked askance, dubious of this psychedelic intruder on their comfortable glumness. Suspicion and mistrust fell like a cloud upon the inhabitants of the town, and everyone kept the café at arm's length, if not further. Everyone but Holly.

Our Christmas christened heroine lacked the pessimism of her peers. She stood, nose pressed against the glass, breath fogging the windowpane of the cereal café as her eyes tracked the multicoloured packages lined up tantalisingly upon the shelves: a kaleidoscope of flavours just waiting to be unwrapped.

Holly was the first, the breaker of the seal if you will, and gradually more visitors stepped tentatively across the threshold, reassured by her jubilant grin, her air of contentment, the satisfying clink of her spoon against the chunky, hand-painted bowl.

Before long, the place was packed, full to the brim of chattering guests, an intoxicating buzz of merriment permeating the walls, the floor, the people themselves, until they left, one by one, smiling and satiated. In no time at all it was the talk of the town: the Tiny Tim of tearooms, dealing in saccharine sweetmeats and a side helping of wholesomeness. By the time the week was out, the town was hooked.

Those sugar-coated claws had sunk so deep into the citizens' hearts that at the crucial turning point their eyes were off the ball. Glued to treats in pudding bowls, they blinked and clinked, and Holly was no more. A second gone, and on and on, as brand-new cartoon packets sprung up around the walls. As quick as it had won them round, so swift was their disposal.

A fortnight passed, the doors were closed, and monochrome glumness descended upon the town like an old and welcome friend. Into the empty streets, the silent houses, creeping through the betting shop's lazily swinging door, the rats came out to play.

Antagonizing the Flock

Courtney Harler

The geese, they gather at the lake in the desert in the winter, burrowing into the reeds and honking into the skies. They come in for landings, skidding along the surface and breaking the thinnest of layers of ice on only the coldest of mornings.

The edges of the lake are dark with frost, the sparse grass blackened by the temperatures that plummet just before sunrise. The wind is a wilderness of its own, sweeping ripples toward the geese – white and brown and gray, with orange beaks.

I watch their feet when they waddle on land, their fat bodies too buoyant for walking long distances. I crowd them and they hiss, then hasten to flight, barely, low to the ground and flapping only far enough to outpace me. I feel the heat of their wings, the heat of their hatred for me – an interloper antagonizing the flock.

The geese tolerate the coots, maybe even welcome their odd little noises. It's biological, I'm sure, or symbiotic in some way. A woman in an SUV once drove up to the lake, right through the park's grass, then scattered bags of feed. I hope she knew what she was doing – I hope she, in fact, worked for the park. Most signs say not to feed the wildlife, not to disrupt the natural order of events.

It's the natural order I'm trying to preserve here. I come here to remember, to observe, to be less, and more, of a person in the world – a woman who matters. You wouldn't think to find a lake like this in the desert, much less one completely overrun by waterfowl. Don't they know it's dangerous here? Cacti and scorpions. The mallards are the bravest, I suppose, their neck feathers iridescent in sunlight.

In My Father's House
Nic Hale

There was nothing more I could do so I decided to interview the creaky floorboard in my father's house. The one just outside the bathroom door that announced his every trip to the loo, and his increasingly aided footsteps.

I sat at the top of the stairs, close to where my head had once stuck fast in the spindles. Behind me, the bedroom door was newly closed, the horrors behind it muffled.

I took a deep breath and tried to form my first question. The floorboard eyed me, warily. It said it didn't know, it wasn't a doctor, after all. To my next question, it snorted,

'No, but you could remind him to dry his hands on a towel, and not just shake them as he leaves.'

'Okey-doke,' I said, and the floorboard looked pleased with our progress. I scribbled down its responses and wiggled aside for the paramedic to shoulder past.

Later, when it was time to sell Dad's house and split the proceeds with my sister, I paused to say goodbye, and the floorboard groaned.

'No one who likes carpets.' I promised, 'No matter what Dawn says.' The floorboard agreed.

I looked back for the last time, glad we'd had that little chat.

The Puncture
Lauren Collett

We'd left the front door open that morning, to air the room, so it's possible – no, probable – that he had heard our shouting, but what choice did he have? There's not another soul within walking distance. That was the draw, way back when.

How long had he been standing there, in our porch? In yellow lycra so tight that I could see the indentations of his chest hair, like fossilised worms? He held up a limp inner tube by way of explanation. At another moment, I might have laughed.

He said: 'May I use a bucket of water?'

Warren took the port glasses out of the plastic tub in the sink. There was nowhere to put them; the cheese plates were still stacked on the draining board, glued together with the remnants of the brie that no-one had liked. *Rubbery*, Daddy had said. Warren handed me the glasses, two at a time, taking care that our fingers didn't touch. I lined them up on the window sill, identifying the ghostly lips: my coral lipstick, Daddy's wide guffaw, Cynthia's red. Warren's thin lips left almost nothing. You'd barely know he was there.

Warren half-filled the tub and took it out to the porch. I followed; what else was there to do? We both watched as the cyclist crouched on his haunches in front of the tub, submerging the tube bit by bit. I thought of intestines. Warren breathed loudly through his nose, trying to calm himself.

Suddenly, a sign of life – bubbles gasped to the surface. A drowning, in reverse.

'Gotchya,' said the cyclist.

He was prepared; he had everything he needed. A patch, a pump, a towel. A handshake each, and then he left. We both stood in the doorway and watched as he disappeared down the dappled lane, his yellow back flashing alarmingly between the shadows, as if our secrets were waving goodbye.

Do Not Tell Me We Are Friends
Alice Franklin

In the four weeks we have known each other, we have bought each other two books. I have read one of those books and sent you my favourite quotations from said book. You have done the same. We have followed each other on Spotify, and I have listened to your playlists, and you have listened to mine. We have written two letters to each other and, in those letters, we wrote down our favourite lyrics from our favourite songs. We have slept together twice.

Do not tell me that we are friends. Friends don't struggle through books from a genre they typically dislike. Friends don't listen to music from a genre they typically dislike. Friends don't send each other letters when WhatsApp exists. Friends do not sleep together. Twice.

Do not tell me that we are friends as we are crossing the Euston Road. It's too loud here to digest the fact that we will not be having dinner with my friends and my friends' friends. You will not show me around your hometown in southern Sweden, and I will not show you around the sights of Slough.

Do not tell me that we are friends as I am holding your hand. To do so would make me feel conscious of the fact that I am holding your hand and make me wonder if you are holding mine.

Do not tell me that we are friends, our hands now in our pockets, our future now erased, our past now just four weeks of quotations and music and lyrics and letters I wish I could forget, or, perhaps, remember forever.

Growing in the Dust
Dona McCormack

The oak rockers struck against the worn planks of the porch, thumped, marked time amidst endless blowing dust and robin's egg sky. Hank's booted toes lifted each time the chair floated back, then pressed forward into the gray floor. It was a wonder the balls of his feet hadn't imprinted right into the grains of the wood, two immutable statements about holding and swaying. Kate sat beside him on the white bench. Beneath her shifting hips, thin rattan crunched – she uncrossed and re-crossed her ankles. In her lap, the knot of her fingers resembled a rose. Her eyes reflected the cloudy wind veiling the ground.

Hank tried to silence a cough – precious energy wasted now trying to suppress undead meat that pitched within the cage of his own too-small skeleton. The red hankie cleared his back pocket, and he wiped his lips.

A hawk on the horizon dropped through the dust for its kill. 'You have cancer, my love,' Kate said.

'Ain't got cancer.' He stuffed his red handkerchief back into his pocket.

'Still won't get the tests?'

'The hell do they know? Or you?'

At the beginning of their marriage, she'd just listen to Hank come in at night and choke up the thick, brown sludge he'd spit in the kitchen sink. She tried to hand him a mask, then just a simple scarf to tie around his nose. He said, 'Can't breathe with them things in my face. Or you.' And she couldn't find a way to argue with that. Or him.

It was the dust inside him suffocating him, and they both knew it. But the cancer hadn't yet eaten the spine he made her chew on.

The rose in her lap whitened, reddened. He chewed on her bitter bone, too – every night, a few crumbs of webcap mushrooms cooked into his dinner. It had been three nights – wouldn't be many more, she knew.

She'd found the solution when walking the fallow ten at sunset.

She had crushed a toe on the rock she knocked aside to unearth the soft, pungent flesh. Just a cluster of fate, growing in the dust.

The Best Is Yet to Come

Grace Glen

'Cheer up, love – the best is yet to come.'

The builder says, a surge of spittle lapping at the corner of his lips, his eyes not rising from their position at half-mast. Buttock height, or it will be when I manage to slope past. Unaware I bear witness to our collective reflection in the window of the shop across the road.

I thread through the town in a loop stitch, double backing, tying up the loose ends.

This time will be the last time I tell myself, uttering my end words; *a pound of mince please; sorry this is late; a fine day indeed for this time of year.* The banalities borne to make way for a new beginning.

Bustling into the house, the phone is ringing. My shopping bag gives way in the juggling act, sending milk shooting across the carpet. The baby howls as I unravel him from my chest and place him under the multicoloured monstrosity which has invaded our living room. My mother asks how we're keeping.

I want to tell her that my feet itch, so I pace past midnight. I've befriended a raven perched on a streetlamp out the window, and we converse, or at least I to him. I watch drunk people spill from bars at 3 A.M., and I'm reading a story about rats biting off cows' udders as I nurse her grandson. How I'm disappointed that for a listed building, full of irritating quirks, there's not a single beam to fasten my rope.

We're fine, I say.

My husband's fallen so deeply in love he can't see the sick in my hair, bags under my eyes and the tightly clenched feeling that's taken hold in my now slackened belly. They share a joke as the baby chortles with the joy of newness in a parallel world.

I wake early. Ejected by the baby. He's taken my place nuzzling into the nape of his father's neck. I stand watching snow fall at the window on an apocalyptic world. Taking the bins out I leave the house barefoot, before disappointment arrives, to make fresh footprints in the snow.

Set on You

Paul Karp

'I got my mind. Set. On. You.'

From my vantage on the couch, I can see every toe tap and finger waggle. With Attenborough detachment I'm watching heterosexual courtship in either its first or last stage. We won't know until she responds to his finger nominating her as the addressee of the song and even then lack of interest could be confused for shyness.

The way the scene is supposed to play is obvious. A gentle touch on the arm and then at the faintest murmur of agreement, one spin and a kiss to make real what the heart doesn't dare could be true.

But their bodies are swaying in parallel, a movement impelled by the other but never yielding. His hands are anxious to bridge the divide. She turns, brushing him with a shaded smile in what could be a coy sign of private delight or an attempt to pour cold water on smouldering expectation.

His insistence suggests to me not blind stubbornness, but an attempt to draw on a canon of prior intimacy. These works will soon either be shared with friends or spoiled by the present approach.

We are watching a half-revelation. The missing piece is behind her smile and the turn that seems a long way short of a spin.

The Sweetness of Love

Margot Zwiefka

I had a dream once that I would be slim. Like dancers in their delicate dresses, fleeting over stage, barely sweeping dust in the air, making it shimmer around their ghost-like figures.

Every day I would go on the scales, all my clothes off, feeling cold glass under my feet. I had a notebook I was putting the results in, looking at my crooked table, promising next day would be better. Afterwards, I would go to the kitchen to drink a glass of water, feeling so blissfully empty. Looking out of the window, wondering when my mum was going to be there. Whether she was going to come in. A sharp car honk outside instead, and I dashed out of the door.

'Hello.'

She would be sitting in the car, on a quick break from work to take me to my duties. Always the same automatic turns.

I remember one day when I was twelve, I took a chance.

'Mum, can I ask you something?' A hmm. 'I would like to take some dance classes.'

She glanced at my body, an eyebrow raised, silence. I turned my eyes away, somehow there was a tear. I like to imagine she felt uneasy.

'You have no time for it, do you? With all the school stuff.'

Our parting was always marked by a ritual:

'Here's your pocket money, for lunch.'

I would take a crisp ten-pound note, thinking how I didn't even need that much. But she never asked what I was spending all that money on. I was holding onto it as I was walking into school, hand in my pocket getting warm.

Sitting through classes I would be planning what I was going to buy. First break – first two pounds spent on a sandwich. Second break – a chocolate bar. Third – a fizzy drink. Fourth – a hot-dog. Fifth – a donut.

The sweetness of love. How full of it I was.

Swing As If Your Life Depends on It
Anne Howkins

Nothing but black and grey above her.

Chose well, she thought, clawing back the wire fence where the druggies sneaked in, squeezing awkwardly, finally, through. There'd been days when she'd almost followed them, her old lady handbag full of crisp tenners, ready to experiment with spoons and cigarette lighters. A scavenging fox yowled nearby, sending her heart clattering against scrawny aching ribs. Neighbours complained of her leaving scraps for the gaunt, cub-worn vixen. She hoped the noise had woken them.

Occasionally she dipped clawed bony fingers into the paper bag rustling in her coat, like the bags of Nuttall's Mintoes Grandad shushed into her pocket when Mum wasn't looking. Those weren't to be shared either.

Then, Mum would send her off to the park, 'Be back for tea.' At first it was hop-scotching; screaming on the boy powered roundabout; grabbing Becca's waist as you see-sawed, loading each end with young bodies, until the day it snapped, sending them starbursting away from the park-keeper's 'Oi, you lot!'

Then, the times a shivery cluster of spotty mascaraed girls watching the lads pretend to be George Best, and the snogging and the furtive groping afterwards. Don't forget the snogging.

Then, the park was to be avoided, away from the mummies, clucking over what she couldn't have building sandpit castles.

Then, sitting with George on his dead wife's bench, 'You're looking a bit peaky, are you eating?'

Now, the park creaks and moans its *'Play with me'* pleas of childhoods past billowing in the wind.

She accepts the slide's slippery invitation, hauls her bones to the top of the world, glissades her way to the depths, eyes streaming from the wind.

The gustily fractious swings, always her favourite, call to her.

She swings. She swings the arc of a wee lass, Dad pushing her with roughened coal tainted hands. Her feet kick forward, forward, leaning her back, opening her face to the heavens, laughing at the silver clock frolicking in an eternal game of cloudy peek-a-boo.

She swings high, lets the swing's pendulum arc launch her, sending her spiralling weightlessly up through the black, grey and silver, dissolving into the clouds.

The Ballet Master's Daughter

Barclay Rafferty

The water is always deepest and darkest on the day you learn to swim.

You doggy paddle, molars grinding, eyeballs cracked with forked lightning, splashing into arms outstretched like piers in the shallows, momentarily forgetting that Mum won't let you drown in the fog.

But I did drown.

—jolted upright, stood by my parents' bed, waited for intuition to wake Mum to a vision of her firstborn, fingernails scrunched to a nightdress. I counted each heartbeat till she sensed me there (*fourteen, fifteen...*). And she did, without a word or prod. She lifted threadbare sheets, guided me by the arm, whispered blearily, *Come, child, s'okay.*

Oh, and I've since made peace with the ocean, having spent so many nightmares there.

Cheap single, thanks.

On the top deck, pleather smooth on my thigh, I press fingertips to pulmonary arteries, pick the Granny Smith from my rucksack, and crunch till they stare. I ring my brother, tell him *We're still the kidz.* He talks about Mum. How she spent her final years, palm valleyed to a pencil, scrawling houses, a recurrent theme for folk with Alzheimer's. We argue about its meaning: a longing for home, or just some cognitive decline towards childhood drawing habits.

I tell him how she claimed to be seventeen years old during my last visit. How she chewed on a lipstick they don't sell anymore and sighed, *I'm fucked, aren't I?* How I ignored her, spoke robotically, *Take a piece of fruit with your medicine, Mum.* How she told me to cut the bruises out first. How she flattened the note like a chorus telegraphing the curtain—

I'm fucked.

Dewy nightmares roost till limestone crumbles, sends coastline to the deep, deep end. You only tempt fate till it crushes you like a comedy piano. Then you wade through life trying to avoid the black keys like cracks in the pavement, all dissonant chords and fucked rhythms.

I'm talking like Mum again.

Her voice carries, milkshook in the foam: *I'v_ see_ eno_gh arm_ an_ leg_. Danc_ w_th yo_r he_rt, chi_d.* Then she foxtrots through the fog, *slow-slow, quick-quick—*

Just in time to witness my first and final *grand jeté*.

The Scar Above Her Lip
Faye Brinsmead

Why don't you remember my birth? the ghost of my sister asks.

What can I say? I just don't.

I remember icicles, I say. *Above the back door, melting in sunshine.*

The ghost of my sister turns away.

I remember chocolate patches of earth. Early spring thaw, I say.

The ghost of my sister thins. No more talk of melting and thawing.

We called them the six pine trees, I say. *Though there were more. We picnicked beneath them on a butter-yellow blanket.*

Was I there? she asks. Thickening a little.

Ye-es, I say. *I don't see you. But I think I feel you.*

She seems to want me to go on.

There was Rex, our German Shepherd. He growled and bared his teeth when Dad fed him. The metal dish clanked as he wolfed his dinner.

But what about me? she insists. *Coming home from the hospital. Being bathed on the kitchen table.*

Maple sap ran down the kitchen walls once, I say. *I see Mum bending over a cookbook, muttering. But the sap behaved so strangely. After hours and hours of boiling, stickiness everywhere. Only half a cup of syrup.*

She's thinning again.

Should I tell her I cherish these visits? On nights I can't sleep, when the edges of awareness crimp like Mum's piecrust.

Should I recount her death? How she slowly regained the lightness of the baby I can't remember. How, wasted and weak, she staggered out of hot bathwater, fell.

There, I could say, pointing to the mark above her lip. *That's the scar.*

Then, clinics. Weigh-ins. Fine down sprouting from her blue skin like translucent lawn. Discharged, gripping my hand with hers, all bone. Sitting at her place like a spectre, retching at the sight of food.

The hardly-anything in her bed one morning. Sunlight sliding, the rest still.

She never asks about any of that. Only the void where her story should start.

Don't go, I plead.

Light slices the curtains.

Next time, I tell myself.

I'm a storyteller. I'll just...

But I know that next time the scar above her lip will wring the truth from me again.

The Dream Journals
Sarah Cavar

I am at the gym, large as purple. Here is the apparatus that makes
a jumper of me. I am so little, trampoline so taut, that I can rise
to hit the rafters above, which lay exposed and prepared to receive
my head or its impact. I jump for some interminable dreamtime before mounting the treadmill. It has two tracks, one for each foot,
which move individually and only just out of time with one another.
The treadmill is so wide that I can run with both of my feet on just
one track and room to spare. All is dull violet, neon-yellow. I know
where I am. All are gears a-turning, form-shaped men and women
in their lines. My father is involved.

*

I stand in the big bathroom. The countertops are salt-pink. The toilet tank has a wicker basket filled exclusively with my toiletries,
except for the butt of my father's electric razor, whose black plug
edges its way out the wall-socket. All this stage right, barely visible
in the mirror that fills overwhelmingly with my naked body. Oh,
how it fills! My breasts are so large and long that the nipples – pink,
pointed like bullets – are paper accordions skimming my thighs.
Hanging like slinkies atop the staircase, yes. Pregnant and about to
end things. Dreamself closes my eyes hard, and then opens them,
and the breasts remain. I wake when I am ready to disappear, feel
the color violet.

*

I am two years old and vomiting more than fifty tiny planes at
the 911 towers. My father watches them come out the TV. I may
not have dreamt this. The planes hit all of us, but with the second
tower I hear it get personal. My ovular mouth says *make thine in-
tentions known* waits to receive reply. Although the planes are only
toys, the momentum they gather singeing toward those twin towers, erect Freudian penis-towers that represent American capital-
ism (or something) allows them to make quite a mess. My father,
still in the room, thinks to himself *fuck it's gonna be a day.*

Girl Weaving Rug

Eileen Malone

She promised herself when it happens, she will take the pill. Find
out what it does. The son of the rug shop owner is behind her, rubbing up against her, sniffing her neck even as she bends away from
him, low to the loom, to get away from his body odor.

He brags about apprenticing to be a gem-cutter. Tells her how he
turns up his nose when cutting lapis lazuli for as soon as the stone
comes into contact with the revolving saw it gives off a foul gas odor.
That's how he can tell if it is artificially gold-flecked jasper from
Germany or the sulfur-stinking real thing.

She believes the rug shop owner's son must be the real thing because he stinks like lapis freshly cut.

He offers her a plate of solid pink jelly cubes flavored with rose-
water, dusted with confectioners sugar. Reminds her she belongs
to him. Insists on pushing one between her teeth, his fingernails
rough on her tongue seeking her throat for a gag, which she does on
his finger, which he pulls from her mouth shaking his hand under
her nose, laughing as he shoves her and barks her back to work.

Her mother taught her how to weave patterns like those found
only on magic Persian rugs flying over wine-purple lakes. Then she
sold her for that talent. Sold her as clean. Gave her a cloth purse
filled with capsules of powder to take when the boy's dirty fingernails begin to enter her body.

She holds the capsule in her mouth for a few seconds and then
lets it slide down her throat, feeling a sort of comfort in the act. Soon
indigo flowers break out everywhere in her mind and along every
one of her nerves. Nothing she has ever known was as pleasurable
as this.

She weaves the carpet to slide under her body, lift its four corners as if flying. She rises, up and up into the undulating black-
purple night where mulberry stars are strung one by one on dark
strands. Where from now on, every night will get dark earlier and
stay dark later.

The Kids Built Me a Roadside Memorial
Anika Carpenter

There's a woman in Arizona who knits with dog hair. If you send her loose hair that you've lovingly brushed from your own dog, she'll spin it into wool for you. You can turn Rex, or Cooper, or Dotty into a jumper woven from unconditional love and total obedience.

It takes three hours to fly from Vancouver to Arizona, but I have precious cargo that I won't put in the hold. So I drive for twenty-six hours, with a coffee-to-go flask in the front and ninety-two shoe boxes in the back, shaking and shuddering like skyscrapers in an earthquake.

Laying in bed in the dog lady's guest room, I still feel the movement of the car, or maybe it's her house, old and beaten, dragging itself across the frozen ground to get closer to other houses for warmth.

'Tinned tomatoes and eggs OK for breakfast, Darlin'?' she calls up in the morning. 'Keeps ya belly warm this time of year!'

'You know,' I say, settling at the kitchen table, nudging the powdered egg with a fork, 'they rely on vibrating machines to pollinate tomatoes now?'

'Not these,' she grins showing-off lipstick-smudged teeth. 'Had these since my Georgie past in 1999.' She holds up the tin. Her hands are like mine, furrowed, ring-free. After breakfast, we head to the workshop, where my boxes are neatly laid out on a long wooden table.

'So,' she starts, 'we're gonna knit a shawl, huh?'

'Yes. One I don't mind dying in. A reminder of something precious.'

'Well, that's what it's all about here, Sweetie. OK, show me what ya got.'

I lift the lid of the nearest box. Hundreds of red-tailed bumblebees, crisp and lifeless. In the second, gypsy cuckoo bees, the third moss carder bees...

'Oh, my! They all fulla bees?'

She opens the remaining boxes, checking over the contents.

'Well, there's no brushin' these critters, we're gonna have to shave 'em.'

We finish mid-December. I make it just past Holbrook before a blizzard sets in, disappearing the highway behind icy static. I pull over, wrap my shawl tight around my shoulders. Wind down my window and let the unforgiving flakes swarm in.

The Lantern Women

Karen Ashe

The youngest of them are the Lighters, but not until they reach a certain age and even then only under supervision. The cliff-edge is no place for youngsters on the loose. They partner at first with an older sister or one of the younger aunts. They fetch the lanterns from barns and coal sheds and cellars, stowed there by the Keepers, the elder women, after dawn.

The Watchers sleep in the mornings, after a long, dark night nursing the flames. These are the in-between women, neither likely to rush headlong off the cliff, nor drop into a chin-on-chest slumber. They are on the look-out for them.

They are all of them thankful for the bees, who fled with them. It is said that bees swarm before death; if that is so then these must be spirit bees and their wax gives off ghostly light. So much the better. When the women eat too much honey, their fingertips glow.

Lilia fetches the lanterns from the cowshed. Her mother watches from the window. With a rag dipped in rainwater she wipes the smoke from the inside of the glass. They must be able to see. She trims the wick.

At dusk, they emerge in twos, from cottage and country house alike, candles already lit. They move like the tide towards the cliff, arranging the lanterns as close to the edge as they dare, a linked fence of light.

Lilia sits cross-legged behind her lantern, pulling on the grass. Aunt Heather fidgets beside her, scanning the sea. At the tipping point of dusk and darkness, Heather grabs her arm. Her whisper is urgent. They hear its echo along the line of them. 'Fetch your mother. They have come.'

The women come, Watchers and Keepers alike. They stand three-deep behind the lanterns, with kitchen knives and meat hooks and bees tangled in their shawls.

Fired and Fledged
Cathy Lennon

Just like the Psalm said, I knit you in my womb. As soon as you were pulled from me, arms and legs wheeling, angry-eyed, you seemed a perfect vessel. I learned the hard way that you were not a cup, to be filled from my jug, but your own experimental form. I still thought you would shatter though, if I didn't pad you round with my worries.

You wanted to feel every scrape, every spike and shard. Your clean, milk-white skin was pierced and painted with indelible images whose stories I couldn't read. You flailed away from this nest in fury, and I looked on, head tilted with an uncomprehending eye. You gained altitude, you plummeted from view then rose again. The sky, harsh-white and limitless, consumed my small black speck.

I stopped looking at the horizon, afraid to see a lightning bolt, a tornado, a mushroom cloud. I told myself that freedom is the greatest gift, after life. I blundered through the years, covering things up and packing things away.

Your voice crows down the line, and I'm struck dumb. Until, like the magpie, I manage a raucous kazoo. 'It's you!'

'It's us!' And in the background I hear the cheeping, the infant wails, and that's three of us weeping.

Finishing Line
Ruth Brandt

Not all here is grim. Oil on puddles swirls pink and yellow, and paint streaks bollards, red, white, blue – a victory flag. And on cold days, those days when frost settles inside windows and the ground freezes feet, ice weaves arteries between cracks in the tarmac. See, it isn't so ugly, not when you can sit and gaze a while.

Once I ran fast, faster than fast, with the breeze lifting my hair and whispering freedom, so fast that even God's eyes could no longer follow. Now I stumble and heave myself upright. So I rest, and beyond revs and shouting I hear bells, and beyond the bells I hear a clock chime and sometimes nuns singing.

He follows me here and leans against the wall ten yards away. When I sense he is no longer looking my way, I glance up, and he is picking his nails or his nose, or staring at his groin as though a dragon might appear with breath the colour of the oil and the voice of a sister. And even though his eyes flit to loiter on me, he doesn't notice the frost that sticks my trousers to the pavement and my arse to my trousers until my stench is no longer to be worried about.

Evensong. A psalm. Notes skitter across a puddle, waving the image of the clouded sun. His heels click as he loafs towards me. He pauses for a moment to tease me with his toe before belting me in my belly, my face, my shins, and once again the grass in a meadow stings my legs as I crouch, preparing to sprint. Then, from nowhere, a sunbeam breaks through, its heat thumping straight into my heart, and I'm off, seeping in a rainbow swirl down into the gutter.

Lying

Dreena Collins

It is in the garden, buried deep and warm: asleep. You wouldn't know it was there. It is hidden, swaddled and tight, in rags and a towel. An unlikely thing, lying there. Hidden, like a whispered prayer. A lie.

For two days there had been a problem with the drains. It started with a gurgling growl in the belly of the house. I ignored it. But then there was rising water and a smell; no, a stench – billowing through. It started in the bathroom, and then it spread, as a swarm, an infestation.

I couldn't fix it, and the landlord couldn't fix it, and the plumber couldn't fix it. So, then it was the job of the council.

And they needed to dig up the garden.

Now I am standing here, at the kitchen window. I am looking out onto grass and dead plants. It is there, but you wouldn't know it is there. Though, I had to do it. What did you expect? I am looking out onto the men in yellow jackets, machines, and at the beds with stones and clay like a bag of marbles, a bag of boiled sweets, around the spot where it is buried.

They have started digging, and so it is only a matter of time. They are just a metre away, about to deliver a miraculous reveal – magicians, unlikely archaeologists. Perhaps they will not realise what it is when they uncover it. Perhaps.

And I can hear a beat, a rhythm, reviving, coming back through the air around me, and within me; it is floating through the dust, like guilt. Floating. Drifting into warmth, dissolving.

The numbness had lulled me into thinking I was past feeling. But, no, I remember. And I can feel: I feel again, the urgency, the beating, the rhythm, the tearing.

It was a lie. It was a lie. It was a lie.

Bessie Swann's Estate
Alexina Dalgetty

A heap of photographs in a weary manilla envelope, soft from overuse.

She'd lived life with a smile on her face and a body full of promise. Eyes bright on the camera and lips a ribbon of perfect pink zippered with even teeth and framed by winced up cheeks and a crinkled nose.

School photo. An eager to please cheerfulness beamed from the kitchen table until long after the deadline for orders passed. Bessie shuffled the order form under Mum's nose; Mum shoved it back.

The passport. A key to the world. Bessie radiant with dreams of international modelling. Her smile eclipsed his heart for a month. They crammed themselves into a photo booth at the mall. One strip, two photos each. She heard he went to Spain for his honeymoon.

Her wedding photo, brash and beautiful. Bessie's blossoming maturity shot through with white lace. Later face down on the windowsill, then face down in a cardboard box.

Girls' night out. Bessie radiant between beer stein and wine glass. Drinks in the front row, women in the back, Bessie's smile the leader of the pack, spraying hope and happiness in an evening of lost stakes.

Posed with another woman's husband. A fat bastard liar. An *I should have known better smile*, pleasures gleaned from the barest harvest.

Mug shot. People don't smile on these, said the cop. Bessie couldn't help it; it was what she did. After three tries they went with the version with the more refined smile. One of Bessie's favourites, too bad about the height measure in the background. The charges were dropped – shoplifting, first offence.

Bessie smiled when they buried Jimmy Bean. She should have grinned less and mourned more. Friends and acquaintances whispered behind her back... maybe Bessie and Jimmy Bean... maybe it ended badly... smiling at his grave.

The funeral director shook out the smiles, a bruised arm, the victories, a blacked eye, the pleasures, a scraped rib, a school photo with proof stamped across her forehead.

How to Eat a Plum
Alice Franklin

1. The garden isn't really big enough for a tree, but you buy a sapling anyway. You settle on a plum tree because you both like plums better than any other fruit.
2. In summer, you sit on the bench, bitching about your respective places of work. You are warm from the alcohol by the time it is dark and cold. Sometimes, you remember to water the sapling. Occasionally, you give it beer instead of water. It doesn't seem to mind.
3. In autumn and winter, the garden is ignored. The sapling soaks up the rainwater, ignored.
4. In spring and summer, after the baby has gone to sleep, you sit on the bench and drink cans of beer. Sometimes, you fall asleep outside, but go in before it gets too dark and cold.
5. In autumn, the sapling produces what could be fruit, but they are small and bitter.
6. In winter and spring and summer, the garden is used every day by your kid. He toddles over to the tree, and comes back, his fists full of twigs. They are a present.
7. In spring, the three of you sit on the bench. When he falls asleep on your lap, you carry him inside. You fall asleep just after.
8. In summer, the tree produces real fruit for the first time, but you're too busy inside, so you ignore this.
9. In autumn, the electricity runs out. You have no wood, so you go to the tree and hack off branches. The wood is damp, so the fire doesn't take.
10. In winter, you sit on the bench, drinking alone. Sometimes, you show people around the house and garden. 'That's a plum tree,' you say. 'It produces excellent fruit.'

The Fire Eaters

Philippa Bowe

I didn't want to come because he's been at me with the belt again and the hard benches in the hall bite the back of my legs. He caught me in my brother's trousers and a charcoal moustache. *No daughter of mine...* Familiar refrain, familiar buckle-shaped welts.

But here I am, dutiful me. Light from the oil lamps flickers and dims. Then they appear. Extravagant leotards, jewel-coloured carapaces like exotic beetles, enclosing three women. Gleaming muscles, disorderly hair. The most beautiful thing I've ever seen. Their hands flash, pale fish swimming in the half-dark. Suddenly their chins lift, mouths gape, fiery breath spews. The flames tear holes in the fabric of the air. What I glimpse through them invites, frightens.

All through the night I dream of fire and glittering rubies. When morning comes, my schoolbag ends in a hedge, and I go to find them. They sit outside their caravan draped in tattered silk robes. One, smoking, two, reading a magazine, three, frowning over raggedy nails.

'I want to come with you.' Silence. 'Please, I can't stay here, I... like all the wrong things...'

The smoker sighs, tamps out her cigarette, looks up.

'Sweetie, we've been there. But it's not all beer and skittles, this life. You're just a fledging, you'd fall and break. You need to grow wings.'

'But...'

'Fly away now, little bird, you're annoying us.'

The next morning, armed with unanswerable arguments, I return. To an empty field. I fold onto the flattened grass. But there is a vestige, a box. *For the fledgling.* Within, a pencilled address and a small mirror, its glass greenish, cloudy. I look into it, see a laughing me, a scowling me, endless mes. Endless, blazing horizons. I hold my box tight and cross the fields, feet not quite touching the grass.

Space Dust
Eleanor

I was a star.

Once I was beautiful. Refulgent. Immortal.

I was a star and I was untouchable.

It started with pain. A searing ache through the roots of my lungs, across my trachea, throat and the folds of my brain. Like a liquid, filling the cracks, smoothing the creases. Heavy in its numbness.

I was a star, once, did you know?

Stars don't hurt. Stars don't fall – you know that right?

Those streaming lights in the sky, they're just debris streaking past our atmosphere, waste left by the humans who dared to go further.

They aren't real stars. Just junk. Rubbish. Dead skin sloughed away.

I was a star and I was impossible.

And I fell.

It wasn't a quick thing, not while it was happening, it's only in hindsight that I can kick myself for not noticing that all the stability I thought I had was temporary, scaffolding, nothing meant to last.

You know, in space, there's nothing to hold onto.

You know, in space, the surprised gasp before the fall is met with silence.

I must have been a star, once.

The landing was the nastiest bit. I fell into a forest. Trees, they layer upon one another, the branches weave together to form blankets, thick, green, lush, deceptive. Every layer I thought was the last until the wood splintered and the branches gave way.

I was dirty and bleeding with fistfuls of the leaves I'd tried to hold, I was tired and small and insignificant and all I could think, as

I lay on the floor and watched the sky between the tangled knots of branches, is that I was a star once.

Once, I was a star.

And I was up there, and I was beautiful, and there's gravity – There's gravity, and it makes falling easy, but now I'm down, what's here to pull me back up into the sky?

No ladders, no rope, no physics, no wings.

I was a star once.

I got lost, and I can't seem to find my way back home.

But I promise you I was a star.

By Montparnasse
Elodie Rose Barnes

There is nothing to be done in Paris when it rains. In Paris, unlike anywhere else, even a drizzle can soak you on all four sides and down the middle, chilling you through whether winter or summer. The streets, washed of their bohemian airs and stripped clean of any understated luxury, show off their dirt and grime. The buildings appear sodden to the core, damp seeping in through centuries of stone. Perhaps I am not poetic enough. Paris in the rain is supposed to be romantic, but I prefer to stay dry.

The first moments after the rains have stopped, though – now those are magical.

The city takes its time in revealing itself. First the cobblestones glistening one by one along the street, and then, if you look up, the windows, shining clear in the translucent light and each one holding more lives than you could ever imagine. Gradually the city opens up around courtyards and alleys, spreading over the quais and the river. In the parks, the leaves hold onto droplets, playing with rainbows in the light. Everything comes alive, but very few stop to watch it.

I saw her suddenly one morning, in the last of the rain. Dropped gently from another era with bobbed hair and faded red lipstick, and bringing with her the first rays of pale sunlight through the clouds. She hovered, one foot on the pavement and one off, unsure whether to cross, and for a fleeting moment her whole body hung, suspended. A question, a whisper floating across years and space. *My time or yours.* My answer was to silently raise the camera, and the shutter clicked on another world.

Then a car passed in front, and she was gone. I saw a flash of black coat round the corner, a glimpse of dark hair that shimmered like wet ink. But when I developed the film, all I saw was a shadow in the pale light, the glimpse of a being on the road between the Jardin du Luxembourg and the rue Vavin.

I've seen ghosts since, here, and sometimes I wonder if I've seen them before and not known.

A Curious Herbal

Christine Collinson

I study the quince again, then return to the bench and carefully apply ink to paper. Afternoon sunlight bathing the physic garden draws out the golden-yellow of their flesh. I must remember the precise hue to achieve a true likeness, so that every page can be perfect.

Tomorrow, I shall progress; perhaps to the blood-red Love Apple, perhaps the fragrant Camomile. I'm working with the seasons, anticipating when each blooms or produces fruit. But nature's ebb and flow cannot be hurried; I adapt to it, like a bee that waits for pollen, like a bird that plucks worms after rain.

Alexander will be expecting the next sketches. I'm not naïve about the debtors' prison, but I welcome the distraction and purpose of my work. I observe him reach for the paper with a pale, thinning arm, but we avoid the difficult conversations. Last time I showed him my sketch of St. John's Wort. 'It's excellent, dear Elizabeth,' he said. 'I can tell you plenty, such benefits that it has.'

The garden's a pleasure today, and my spirits lift as Isaac points out the new species under his cultivation. 'From warmer climes across the ocean,' he tells me. I'll certainly include the tobacco plant; expect that Alexander will know it.

Greenery spreads before me in every direction like my own botanical paradise. 'I'd love to travel to distant places,' I say as I watch him take a cutting. 'This corner of London's perfect, isn't it, but it ends at the garden walls.'

Isaac looks at me and smiles. 'God willing, you and your husband will be reunited, and your family will be free to.'

I observe the fresh cutting in his soiled hands, dare to imagine the days and weeks ahead; as now, yearning for continuing light and warmth. As the sun fades, shadows lengthen across the paths, and I sit again, breathing the familiar floral scents. Isaac's gone; I see his back dip through the hot-house door.

Tomorrow I'll return with my ink and paper, to begin the next page.

The Professionals Involved

Cathy Lennon

The Pharmacist who sold me the kits
The Estate Agent who found us the house
The General Practitioner who referred us for tests
The Mortgage Advisor who loaned us the money
The Gynaecologist who could find nothing wrong
The Surveyor who told us it was sound
The Consultant who said we could have one attempt
The Solicitor who dealt with the sale
The Nurse who showed me how to inject
The Removals Men who carried the boxes
The Doctor who said it was positive
The Builder who said he'd give us a quote
The Aerial Fitter who found the body

The Police Officer who called the Forensic Pathologist
Who said it had been dead a long time

The Paramedic who held my hand

The Sonographer who called the Consultant
Who said there was no heartbeat

The Journalist who was only doing her job
The Human Resources Officer who was only doing his
The Coroner who said it might have been stillborn
The Mother-in-Law who said unwanted pregnancies were common
then
The Boss who was an unfeeling bastard but this was a great chance
The Receptionist who didn't know anything about a conference in
Wales
The Locksmith who whistled while he worked
The Trade Union Rep who said it would be difficult
The Estate Agent who put the house on the market
The General Practitioner who referred me for support

The Pharmacist who dispensed my antidepressants
The Counsellor who didn't say anything
Just pushed a box of tissues across the table

The babies who were

Phoenix

Janet Laugharne

I saw the fire pit, smelt the leaves and garden rubbish burning, helped collect the ash. And I thought it was fine.

The skills you learn and take with you from one country to another, from before war to after war. And who knows who you were, once, when you get to that new country?

I was a child then, drawn to the delicious smell of wood smoke and the bright crackle of burning.

Only later did I see it in a different way.

She didn't speak about her past. They weren't interested – or too polite to show it? She was different, solitary, sharing some interests, The Times crossword puzzle, gardening; but different too, no family, no children, no husband, no words about her life before arriving. Her crafts were continentally different, knitted socks on a circular needle, crochet and pickled vegetables.

Her house smelt of paraffin.

I ran through swathes of cold down a thin-carpeted corridor to the one heated room; her wing chair by the open grate and an upright one for me, the guest.

We put carbolic soap, red or green, under our fingernails so we didn't pick up the dirt and dust while we worked, throwing twigs and newspaper on the fire.

She tended it with a stick, prodding it into life, drifts of smoke blue on the air. I was the pupil. She was the teacher.

Only later did I wonder.

No knick-knacks, no extravagances, all neatness. Everything in spartan order.

There was one picture, of her with her companion, the wealthy one, who left her the house, sepia, in long skirts, with guides, climbing the Alps.

They say the guards put soap under their nails, too, a barrier against others' charred remains, but what can block the mind?

Every autumn the fires. In it, leaves that had run their course; budded, blossomed, thrown cool shadows over the summer garden and dropped, withered, to the ground.

She raked them all up for burning. The smoke curled through the bare, hillside trees. Neighbours passed. I helped.

Had she risen, phoenix-like, from fearful ashes, her garden fire so assiduously tended?

Maintaining Dignity When Studying
Has Been Somewhat Slack

Sharon Boyle

Do not cry. If you can't do the swotting, don't do the sobbing. Pupils might not remember the periodic table but they sure as hell will remember your acned, angsty, pink-eyed face weeping over the chemistry paper.

Do not panic. There is no dignity in hyperventilating. This is nobody's fault but your own. (Strike this last if you are sensitive as well as lacking sense).

Do not pretend to faint. Everyone will know you're copping out no matter your well-crafted contradictions when you 'recover'.

Do not copy other students' papers. This is cheating. Invigilators are attuned to the prickling desperation and rotating eyes of someone primed to sneak a cheeky glance.

Do not doodle. Or worse, write rants. Or worse, jot jokes. Or worst of all, compile an essay on the tortured history of self, explaining why self was prevented from studying and should be awarded marks for the act of turning up.

Do remember this sinking sensation. Harness it, cherish it even. Think, *this feeling is unwanted, and more importantly, unnecessary*. Admitting that you should have perused, memorised, even crammed the topic in a one-nighter, is a step forward on the self-help path.

Do turn your ears to cloth when the exam is over. Rise from the chair and do not listen to the instant chatter that will also rise. Ignore all *Did you get such and such?* or, *Wasn't as bad as I thought it would be.*

Maybe you'll be lucky enough to scrape through, just, jinxed with a scant *Pass*, awarded on a scrap of paper, fixed, non-erasable, a stain of ink declaring you lax.

Maybe.

But know this for definite – for as much as you detest sitting tight with a ploughed-up brow while all around you pencils skim, wrists glide and sheets of paper spawn words – hundreds and thousands of words – while your paper lies barren, remember that you hate the concepts of application, concentration and the notion of vocation even more.

Do therefore resign yourself to next year. Same place, same subject.

Overgrown
Jim Toal

You've started smoking again, but you're too worried to care.

Your cigarette butt arcs beyond the decking into the jungle of weeds it took years of grim determination to tame. Remember? It doesn't seem to bother you that everything has gone to seed. Like you, returning to unbridled nature, oozing sappy poison, tangled with barbs.

Without comment, you drink the *special* coffee brewed from the Burundian beans you always made such a fuss about.

You read your girlfriend's note again, and again, as if repetition will decode a hidden message. It mentions her departure, nothing else. You confess to searching her hosiery drawer. Her diaphragm is missing. Instead of recoiling from such disgusting intimacy, I encourage, nodding like a fool.

Your diagnosis of pancreatic cancer brought us back together, briefly, but I realise it can't last. I despise her treachery, and, in an aloof, despairing way, hold *her* responsible for your demise.

You're to blame, you say. You're desperate to know her whereabouts, who, why?

You are hers. I concede. Already your brow beads mortuary liquor like rotting fruit in a bowl.

In silence, a fog of naked thought knits between us.

Always too kind, you say. Too patient. You stand to leave. That ironic smile insinuating I've heard enough of your troubles.

But it's difficult to eradicate weeds. Water hemlock still grows by the stream. Its parsnip-scented oil burrows deep into the nervous system.

A spider voice crawls from my throat. Stay if you like, I say, knowing you won't.

Thanks, you say, but you'll keep me awake treading furrows in the carpet.

Truly, it saddens me that I won't be there for you.

You better get back, you add. She might call round. You can't miss her.

At least have another cup of coffee. No, I insist.

By your car, we hug. You tremble. So thin, now, I can strum your ribs. How long? I wonder.

As I stand, watching your car depart, a fat, glossy fly lands on my wrist. Crawling onto an anniversary bracelet worn specially, it gathers up its legs and rubs them together. Too quick for my swatting fingers, it springs into the air.

How to Buy Books When You Don't Read Books
Alice Franklin

1. Buy literary magazines and struggle through overly long essays on authors you don't recognise who come from countries you also don't recognise.
2. This is why you are going to read. Eventually, you will know where Moldova, Tuvalu and Honduras are. What a day that will be.
3. Think harder. Decide that 'literary fiction' means you can read whilst sipping vodka martinis in dimly-lit bars wearing unnecessary glasses, not getting distracted by the free jazz playing in the background.
4. Search for independent bookshops. After all, if a stranger approaches you in the dimly-lit bar whilst you are sipping a vodka martini and wearing glasses not getting distracted by the free jazz, you want to say you bought this obscure tome from an obscure shop from an obscure man who manages to use the words 'supercilious', 'desultory' and 'ubiquitous' all the in the same transaction.
5. Google what the words 'supercilious', 'desultory' and 'ubiquitous' mean.
6. Settle for an author who's Albanian. Buy a map of the world and, after ten minutes of scouring it, place a pin on that tiny country.
7. Imagine a man dressed in black entering your dwelling, examining the map, asking you if you have travelled to all these places. 'No,' you will say. 'These are all the countries I have *read*.'
8. Go to the bookshop. Get shouted at for wearing a backpack.
9. Pick the Albanian man's book off the shelf and go to the counter.
10. Go home, leave the book on your bedside table. In the following months, do not read the book by that Albanian author. In the following months put the Japanese word *tsundoku* into practice. In the following months, place a pin on the countries you have neither read nor travelled to.

Every Morning
Louella Lester

Those who had little curiosity, like her husband and two sons, would say that the view out the living room window never changed much. But she knew different. And, as soon as she was tall enough to see over the windowsill, her daughter knew it, too.

The sun had been up for two hours, though hidden somewhere behind the thick cloud. Edie had already made breakfast and packed lunches. Checked that children were clean, clothing was tidy, and homework was in backpacks. Pulled something out of the freezer and set it on the counter to thaw for supper. She kissed her husband before he left for work in the city. Kissed her two sons before she shooed them out the door. While she washed dishes, she'd watched out the kitchen window to make sure they made it to the school bus. Thought about the living room window and the chair, her chair, the only one that didn't face the television.

She had dried the dishes and shelved them. Swept the kitchen floor dirt into the dustpan and dumped it into the garbage can near the door. 'Nina,' she called her youngest, the only one still not old enough for school. 'It's our time now.' Nina left her doll under the kitchen table and flew to the living room ahead of her mother. She stopped near the window. Edie pulled open the drapes. Dropped into the chair and pulled Nina onto her lap. They both smiled, but they didn't speak.

Out the window, the barbwire was barely visible between the grey, slightly angled, fence posts. The grasses and reeds moved like waves on a wind-tossed lake. The tree stood out on its own above distant bushes and the flat marsh. It was all pretty much the same as it had been yesterday and the days before that. But mother and daughter, still silent, waited.

Then Nina raised her arm and pointed her finger. 'Yes,' whispered her mother, 'I see it.' And they both watched as a lone pelican soared on wind pockets above the tree. Became the day's difference.

Hare's Breath

Tracy Fells

The night before my mother's trial I see the hare. I watch from behind a spoil heap of dank, damp earth. It pays no heed to my presence, continuing to dance between the gravestones in the moonlight.

Despite Father's pleas they hang my mother like a criminal, swing her high at the crossroads.

WITCH

The townsfolk hiss and spit like cats as they cut her down from the noose. When her body later disappears from the burial cart, they blame my father and brothers for stealing her back.

WHORE

At dusk I return to the graveyard and wait, my back pressed against a stone slab crusted with lichen. I sense the hare, tasting my scent in the silence. Its outline a twitching silver shadow. I hold out a trembling hand, whispering the words she had taught me. The hare's warm breath teases my fingertips, testing if I am friend or foe, soft like a mother's kiss.

WOMAN

The drumming of men's voices echoes in the stillness. At first like a growl of distant thunder, then rising in pitch as they thrash through the boundary copse, baying like a pack of starved hounds. The hare's black eyes shine, she twists away from my touch and runs into the long grass that hides her like a shroud. I sing a blessing to the moon; crouch onto all fours. With my ears laid flat against my back, I spring forward, stretching out my forelimbs, pushing off my hind legs, muscle and sinew slipping into one fluid purpose: to flee. I no longer see the other hare, but I can smell her as clear and distinct as fresh laundered linen.

I follow her scent, follow my mother into the night.

Beta Vulgaris
Jude Higgins

He told her he was depressed, so she lavished him with beetroot – boiled, pickled, juiced, roasted, sliced cold in salads and she cooked beet greens instead of his favourite vegetable, broccoli.

'Beets were offered to the god Apollo,' she said. 'Did you know that they are one of the oldest crops grown for human consumption?'

He didn't know this.

She told him beetroot was full of antioxidants, vitamins and minerals, helped asthma, cleansed the blood, balanced blood pressure and would be good for his eyes as well as his depressed feelings.

'There's nothing wrong with my eyes,' he said. Although it was hard to look at her when she was so eager to make him feel better.

In the outside toilet, now his refuge, he noticed his urine, and everything else besides, had taken on a pinkish hue. This made him feel bad about her and worse about himself.

The same day, she consulted Wikipedia again and told him the Romans had offered Aphrodite beets. They were rich in boron, which promoted a feeling of wellbeing. Beetroot would put fire in his veins. She cooked them borscht for dinner. Her face was radiant as she ladled out the soup, but her hands trembled.

'Did you know that at the end of the Space Race the Russians served borscht to the Apollo 18 astronauts?' she said, her voice louder than usual.

He didn't know this.

On his birthday, she made a large and succulent beetroot and chocolate cake and invited over some old friends to help celebrate his life. She went to fetch them from the station.

He wasn't there when they got back.

A Fairy Tale for Singletons
Donna L Greenwood

When Mark Crofthouse finished with her, she decided to stop biting her nails. It was probably the way she spat out her nails that drove him away.

At eighteen, she met another Mark. Slim hips, cool car. He liked her laugh. *Some girls are frightened of laughing messily*, he said, *but not you*. When he dumped her, she gave up laughing.

Christopher Jones promised to marry her. He loved her curves; he couldn't wait to see her in white. *Perhaps she could lose a bit of weight off her hips?* Two months later, he left her at the altar. After that she stopped eating until every one of her ribs popped through her skin.

Tom, Brian, Alex, Dave, Brian (again), the man from Funnies night club, that taxi driver (twice), two Andrews and a Steve.

Over the years she stopped:

reading, wearing black, smoking, smiling, liking cats, singing, coughing, wearing pyjamas, fidgeting, writing, dancing, telling jokes, wearing trousers, swearing, wearing eyeliner, dying her hair blonde,

until the only thing she had left was her breath.

Then Gary came along and made her breathless.

But something happened with Gary.

Gary said,

Christ, could you breathe any louder?

And she was just about to suck in her breath so that it would stream quietly from her nostrils, when her mouth took on a strange shape. Her teeth jabbed her bottom lip, and a slow fricative began to form, followed by an Anglo Saxon vowel and, to her delight, the words

FUCK YOU

fired from her mouth.

Gary left, and she let out a breath she'd been holding for years.

Now she holds her fat belly and laughs; she reads, swears, coughs, dances, goes to bed when she wants, writes poetry, sings to her cats and breathes with her mouth wide open.

Black Dog

Annalisa Crawford

I have a black dog. With bottomless brown eyes that impede me wherever I go and ears that prick at every unexpected noise. He rests his head in my lap to remind me he's there and nuzzles against my leg. Sleek, majestic, wily.

When I shower or take the bins out or shovel laundry into the washing machine, his nose is rammed against my hand, manoeuvring me to focus on him. He almost purrs.

Yet once I've patted him and said Good Boy, he won't quit. He nudges my hand, pushing upwards when I'm carrying hot drinks. He nips my calves to hurry me along or slow me to a torpid crawl. He whines and yaps in aggravated bursts; a constant reverberation in my head.

My black dog lumbers around the house, flopping onto the floor to trip me when I try to cross the room, burying my blister-pack medication in the garden, thwarting my enervated attempts to do anything at all. A stubborn weight sitting on my chest.

We go for walks, my dog and I, just to get some peace. He sprints for sticks and chases squirrels up trees. We frolic feverishly through parks and streams and all along the lanes that circle our town. Sometimes there are not enough places to be. No matter how many hours we're out, he's still bouncing off the walls when we return while I lie down, exhausted, and can barely feel my limbs.

Alert all day, howling all night. An incessant drone drilling my skull. I sneak off without him, hiding behind shrubs and fences, holding my breath in case he can sense me with his acute intuition. He's not fooled. He hunts me down like it's a game. Sitting and waiting, his head cocked to one side.

Abruptly, for days or weeks at a time, he coils motionlessly into a snug circle, nose tucked beneath his tail, and snores like a mollified baby; but the serenity is tentative, and I wait for the fracture.

Your Body Built Me

Clodagh O'Brien

I know you don't want me. Alone in the dark, I know. Better than you know. Because you're not ready yet; to admit it, but your body is, and I am your body. Your body built me.

I don't have a name, will never be given one. So I make one for myself. Let letters slide over my not yet tongue. It's *L's* I like. The way they have to click before being said. I am a girl, and my name is Leila which means night, because I live in the dark and came from a night that should have had love. Instead, it was fast and muffled and full of rips that shredded your soul.

I curl my fingers and toes to swim. Roll into ripples that make you lurch and sink to your knees at the toilet bowl. When your breaths are calm I float to the wall and stroke you. Press my fingerprints against your insides as if searching for ink. Sometimes I feel you, see the dark tentacle stretch of your hands above me. But your holds are so brief; I wonder if they happen at all.

Outside there are voices. Not yours; too low, too calm. You scream at them for something to scream at. They hold onto their words. Repeat them as if you are deaf. They say things that upset you, so unsettle me. My home churns in yo-yo bursts. I hold onto our cord and imagine I am a boat, anchored to the bottom of a sea I'll never see.

I know you might want me. If things were different. If I was a choice, not a consequence. I am your body. Your body built me.

What Gets Left Behind

Anika Carpenter

A Chrysanthemum morifolium has around seven hundred and fifty petals. This is the kind of thing you learn working as an artist's Studio Assistant. I was one of a team of five, three artists, a musician and a friend of a friend of the artist, employed to make a ten-foot by ten-foot flower.

In a warehouse, much larger than we needed it to be, we listened to the radio, drank tea, and transformed eighty yards of ripstop nylon into an avalanche of oversized petals. When I told people about my job, they'd say: 'I bet you see petals in your sleep'. I dreamt I was a kid scared of vicious insects hiding in fist-sized blooms, and of monstrous earwig bosses clacking their pincers like castanets.

On Fridays, the five of us treated ourselves to a greasy spoon lunch. On a wall-mounted telly, we watched police firing water-cannons at kids protesting against climate change. Rolling text confirmed that they'd all be expelled from school and their parents fined more than they could afford. After that, it turned my stomach to be working on something so ruthlessly delicate, so deceptively pristine.

*

I've brought my daughter to the abandoned sculpture park to show her the special thing I made, 'Before I even knew Daddy!' It's speckled with mould now and looks more like a sparrow's breast than a Chrysanthemum. I circle it, try to identify a petal that I'd made so that I can say 'this one, this is mine'. They all look the same. Pressing one between my fingers, I wonder what songs I'd listened to on the day it was made. Had I cycled home in the rain that day, met a friend for dinner, was it the day I'd had a row with my sister or slept with the guy who designed aeroplane seats? What I recalled clearly was that I lived with five other women in a four-storey Georgian House. My hair was cut short and, when I bought flowers, I wished they still came wrapped in paper. Thin florist's paper that as you smoothed it out, made the sound of the surf on pebbles.

If Light Is Measured in Magnitude, How Do We Measure Dark?

Johanna Robinson

Annabel crouches in the wild corner of the garden, still in her dressing gown, which is hemmed with twigs and mud. It's the garish one that her family detests; they shade their eyes from her each morning, half in jest. Paul has strimmed, trimmed and planted the rest of the garden – the lawn that she thinks of as a torso, the two rockery shoulders. He tends it as though it was *him* who had always lived here. Once, Annabel tweaked out the white plastic labels from under each plant and stuck them back at random.

She divides the bramble curtain, as a badger might, head down, all paws, and crawls in. Thorns nip on her yellow towelling sleeves. Inside the den, the branches cut the sky into chevrons. On her knees, she scoops away the topsoil. The stone bed is cold. She scrapes at leaves, clumped and rotten, or green and bug-eaten. A spider tickles the soft veins of her wrist. She lowers herself onto the flat slabs, onto her back. Her fingers stroke a tree root that has ventured above ground. The cold demands most of her thoughts; she closes her eyes. 'You will need this, one day,' her mum had said when Annabel was seven. 'Help me.' They had lugged and aligned the stones, their muscles growing walnut-hard, dust in their eyelashes.

'It looks like a grave,' Annabel had whispered.

'The opposite.' Her mum shook her head. 'A god needs a bed of stone for when they need to sleep. If you build the bed, they come. Our job is to keep it warm for them.'

'What will he want?'

'Not he,' she'd said. 'She.'

Annabel waits. She never lies like this: quiet. Never sits without an eye on the second hand. Never notices the colour of the inside of her eyelids. Always scared to see what might happen if she stops *being there*.

After minutes, or perhaps hours, the god arrives, just as her mother had promised.

'What do you want?' asks Annabel, after all these years of wondering. The god's touch is like moss across her eyes.

'The same as you,' she says. 'Rescue.'

Tourists

Isaac Sleadd

A diamond is falling in the streets of Paris, away from a broken silver clasp and the neck of a woman named June. It strikes a cobblestone, then settles into a crack beneath the wheel of an abandoned car. 'Mark,' she says, but her husband is a block away, filming a wall of graffiti. *Always with that damn camera. Never here when she needs him.* 'Mark!' she cries. He switches off the camera and saunters over. *Lazy fuck.* She is down on all fours, clawing at the earth in a flash of desperation. Dirt in her fingernails. Blood. *Bloodline. Her family was right. She never should have married this art student from Omaha, with no practical skills and his head in the clouds – 'an ideas kind of guy.' What a joke.* 'I can't reach it,' June chokes, tears dribbling from the end of her nose. *She is a little girl, bent over Grandma's knee beside a cow pasture. Her pigtails bounce when the paddle strikes home. This is what she gets for touching Grandma's jewelry box. This will teach her to be more respectful.* Mark taps at the stone with the quill of a pigeon feather, nudging it closer in the crack between the cobblestones. He almost has it, but it slips. 'God damn it!' June says, and turns her back on him. *She is a young woman, standing before an open casket. Grandma is laid out in her sky-blue pantsuit, her diamond necklace glittering. She shouldn't take it.* She shouldn't have taken it. The feather catches the stone just right. Mark rinses the diamond in a puddle and hands it to June. *She is an old woman, lying in a casket of her own. The diamond is hidden beneath a black velvet dress. Nobody is coming.* 'There, there,' says Mark. *She is in hell, listening to Grandma tell the same story over and over: 'I wanted to travel, but I never left Nebraska...'* Mark kisses June on the forehead. 'Shh,' he says. 'Everything is fine. Everything will be fine.' This precious work of art he must hold around the edges.

A Girl's Guide to Fly Fishing
Mary-Jane Holmes

It wasn't the fly fisher's fault she got caught up in his line, she was too busy rootling in her handbag for a hanky to be paying attention. She felt the hook at her hairline, the lift of skin at the base of her occiput as she catapulted towards the lake. The water was a shock, cold, murk-green, but as soon as she was submerged, she was in the air again, widgeons scattering, lapwings barrel-rolling. The sensation was akin to how the stomach cadenzas when driving a bump in the road at seventy miles an hour or one of those tight orgasms you feel in the small of the back when you've just met someone, something she'd almost forgotten about.

After a while, the fly fisher reeled her in. 'We're not doing it right,' he said.

'You sound like my husband,' she said, picking minnows out of her teeth.

'It's not you, I was fishing salmon, but this might be trout territory.'

She wrung out her hair; he pulled out a box full of feathers, furs and beads.

His fingers were soft against her skin as he wove the fluff of marabou across her scalp, wrapped black chenille round the wire, tied off the hackle with gemstones until she was the perfect bait.

The fly fisher's touch was as light as a water skeeter, she was as iridescent as a damselfly, but still no catch rose to the surface and then just as he was going to reel her in for the last time, there it was: a prism of scales, mouth a wide O gunning towards her. She grabbed it by the gills, kissed its puckering lips, felt the fizz of oxygen between them, the lift of the rod back onto dry land.

Shoebox of Thunder
Barclay Rafferty

Wren song glitches, crackles, drowns in spray-rain, tattoos the shell of the tunnel. I tap its millipede-in-hobnail-boots rhythm on the tiller. Sodden paper chokes a bottleneck, gargles: *If caged birds dream of clouds, what do wild birds dream of?* I place this melting folk wisdom with the other empties, chiming like the Moon.

Goodbye, Gene Cernan, final Earthling, goodbye.

I've always wanted Dreams, not Real Things. When they pan out worse, I turn to the in-between: my computer. It tells me why I'm sick; points me in the direction of the next virtual orgy; gives me knowledge no human ever could. I even stream a live cam from some beach where rowboats jigsaw and elbow the seaside.

But this little grey box can't buzz hair overgrown like spider silk, loosen bowlines, part leaves from trees traced by the Vampire of Summer. Doesn't appreciate wren song that can make your cheekbones shatter.

I pull over, let some bloke overtake, feel the hull of the boat rubbing against silt. He looks baffled. *I can explain*, I don't say, call myself a twit in a homemade grave, ask him to toss some of those eggs he's flogging from his rooftop. Or a life jacket.

His eyes, tree hollows with nothing scurrying, remind me of—

Dad, old lift-shaft peepers himself, stopped turning blackstuff one morning, took a 15p bus ride to Orgreave, picket in hand. Mum dragged herself downhill from the Convent, crossed the border to avoid a life of silent contemplation. Both joined the Natural Causes Club while I drummed the bodhrán to the pissed and prostrate in pub lounges.

I stop by Booth's Garden Nonsense. *Any wharf in a storm* and all that. A cuppa then onto the mooring: berth the narrowboat, fetch logs, tend to violets, orchids—

I know lightning only strikes twice in Dreams, but tonight I'll be standing under tall trees waving golf clubs at passing bolts. And there's still time for you to send that SOS: bottle, skywriting, whatever. No address, just the Shoebox of Thunder. If I haven't returned from the nineteenth hole, just let yourself into the cabin.

You won't need a key, just a skeleton.

Beautiful Beginnings™ Nappy Pins, 10 Pack
Maxine Davies

1. Towards the end of her life, our grandmother came to suffer from the unique delusion that she was made entirely from glass; we approached her only with extreme caution. Three years she lay there, as still as possible, feeble arms placed lightly at her sides. We perched at the edge of her jacquard weave bedspread and offered her water through a straw. Her hair was kept twisted up into a pumpkin with a hairpin, rose gold and fitted with a single freshwater pearl, a wedding day gift. Each evening our mother would loosen her hair, the colour of a ten pence coin, and brush it out against the pillowcase with a boar bristle hairbrush. We leant in close, the soft crackle of it as it smoothed over the tangles, watching mother's gentle hands fasten the pin back into place.

2. I found a handwritten note in my bureau drawer, underneath my smalls. It read: *'See a pin and pick it up, all the day you'll have good luck; see a pin and let it lie, bad luck you'll have all day.'* I put the note into my pocket for safekeeping.

3. The first man I ever loved was a dancer in the National Ballet. He was strong enough to make me feel all of the ways of being small, sometimes stopped short in the street to haul me over his shoulder into a fireman's lift, a practical joke, then let me slip down his front and wrapped his arms around my waist. I was sorting laundry one afternoon when I noticed that the straps of his leotard had been adjusted, folded over and temporarily fastened with two of the Swan Queen's bobby pins.

4. My sister called me Dottie because of the spots on my arms and torso. She didn't know that the marks were self-inflicted.

5. The world turned into rust. I never had the chance to worry about the fastenings coming undone and them spearing the baby in the night. I packed them away with the rest of her things, small bundles of cotton the colours of cake icing.

Filleting Cod

Anne Wilson

It's an art, filleting a cod. You need nimble fingers, precision, practice. One slip of the blade can sever a finger. An observer is unnerving unless you want to impress them with your technique.

Alistair slaps a fish as long as his arm onto the harbour wall, feet planted slightly apart, tongue-tip protruding – an expression I know well. His fingers glide over the slick skin, blade prowling, slower than usual deciding where to cut. The woman leans into him, her hand resting on his shoulder. To delay the crucial moment, he taps out cod anatomy with the knifepoint – *the head, the cheek, the body*. Her crimson lips form an 'o', and her eyes widen into his face. Her hair ripples every time she nods. Just two random strangers transfixed by the corpse of a cod.

He starts by caressing the cheek, tracing a curve below one mournful eye. The blade pierces the skin with a wet pop as he saws a jagged circle round the cheekbone. He eases the flesh away and offers it like a trophy, soft and white on the flat of his hand. She strokes the flesh gingerly, and her lips widen into a smile as he slips it onto her hand. Cradling the head, Alistair prises away the second cheek and lays it tenderly beside the first. He reaches for her other hand. *Feel how firm it is*, he says. Her outstretched arm lifts one breast closer to his nose.

Delicately, he slices the whole side and pulls it away, revealing a pearl ladder of bones. Skin down, the side smacks the stone. The flesh glistens as he slips his knife under the meat and tears away the skin. Now he leans over the fish, teasing the cod worms with the tip of his knife and flipping them onto the dock. She recoils in mock horror, and he laughs. Prick, flip, laugh. A bravura performance.

The carcass – flayed, exposed, discarded – weeps blood onto the stones. Seagulls will pick it clean in a moment. Its senseless eyes stare up at the sky.

My skin prickles hot as I search the horizon. Time to walk away.

A Fantastic Banality

Thomas Malloch

Most days he disappeared to the garden-room to write his break-through fantasy. At least, that's what he told me. And then came a day when he disappeared altogether. A missing person whose personal effects weren't. No clues. No trail to track.

How to grieve this missing husband? Anger, mostly. Kübler-Ross and Kessler Stage 2. Intended for the absent target but caught by whomsoever was around. No surprise then, that as time passed, more and more of my days were spent alone. Often in the garden-room, watching whatever grabbed my attention. Rain-drop tears on the panelled glass; a thrush extracting snail meat from a beautifully broken spiral shell; or today, a ripple at the corner of my eye, as if the canvas of reality had momentarily lost its stretch.

You have to wonder about those flickers at the edge of vision. Their causes. A small bird, perhaps? Flying out from the climbing rose? Possibly. And by such acceptance, the issue is closed. But not today. Today my eyes are drawn to the split in the uPVC at the bottom right-hand panel of the French window.

I get out of the chair and kneel. Then pick at the split with my thumbnail until I can insert a finger and pull. There is a noise like Velcro as the corner of reality's canvas is torn from its frame. The garden scene is peeled back to expose a room, a mirror-image to the one I'm in.

And there he is, sitting in a Lloyd-Loom chair, identical to the one that I'd been in, head in his hands at being found out in this, his fantasy.

I taste the complexity of the moment. The sweetness of a mystery solved. The salt grain of a new world discovery. The bitterness at being left behind. But what comes to dominate is the sourness of disappointment. Such scope for the imagination and what do we get? A re-creation of a room you'd left behind.

George Izzard Fell Asleep
Philip Berry

George Izzard 'fell asleep' in 1920. He was eleven. Yellowed with lichen, shallowed by time and the drip, drip of acidity, I find the mason's work is best understood with fingertips. The stone leans forward and dips to the right in soft ground, as though drawn to magnetic palms. Like every boy, George went through a phase of wanting to conjure and impress.

On a rectangle of combed gravel stands a blue ceramic duck in bell-bottoms, a sailor's jacket and a cocked hat. He looks out over his cartoonish bill, at a scaled-down windmill with moving parts, a model aeroplane, and two squat vases overtopped with drooping blooms. All so delicately positioned. Who did this?

You revere him now as he was then, on the day influenza broke his strength, the hot broth his mother carried upstairs cooling by the wainscot. His younger sister, forgotten at this time of crisis but aware of developing tragedy in an abstract way, peered in from behind the doorpost. But he is over 100 now. He is no longer a boy. He doesn't need these tokens. Let him be.

George Izzard sucks cool morning through the gravel inch, through the fathom of thrown earth, through the collapsed panels. He drinks the fresh, dewy air in the morning, tastes the colour of modernity. He uses the atmosphere as his vocabulary.

George hears her arrive. She comes once a month. A parallel and distant relation without a name. He senses the ground's subtle compression beneath a folded knee and a sensible shoe. New flowers; she bins the old. A model aeroplane – she guesses his current enthusiasm. Eleven-year-olds *like* planes.

I don't know you, mouths George. *What do you owe me? I ceased to be a child when my lungs filled with froth, and I gasped for air beneath my mother's love-filled frown.* He turns these words out of the wind and the leaves. She darts her head to the phrase, studies an oak's foliage… but the message has already flown. She places the aeroplane carefully, as though lining it up on a runway.

I take it, and break it.

Pleasing

Ned Carter Miles

I gag a little on the pill and bend down to suck at the faucet, cursing my wants, cursing my cock, loving my wife.

'What's taking so long?' she calls. I've left the bathroom door open a few inches, but her voice barely carries now. I hide the pack with its one torn blister and come back to bed. She's turned away, and her ribs ripple under her skin as she breathes.

Please know I want you.

I shuffle up behind her where before I'd pull her to me, surrounding her carefully. Her belly is tissue paper.

'This is my favourite place to be,' she says.

'Mine too.' And yet my throat is swelling.

She presses into me with small strength and familiar intent. The question her body's asked mine a thousand times: 'Are you awake? Are you awake to me?' and I'm bitter for every one of them I chose the better night's sleep. I arrange myself, limp, between her wasted buttocks, and she nestles. She used to demand I slap them so hard that, being the stronger one, I worried I'd hurt her. She said she liked the marks.

Let me give you this.

'Are you going to?' she asks, and I bury my face in her hair, which has thinned, imagining it dissolve in my mouth like ash or candyfloss. I close my eyes and picture her as she was, betraying her as she is now – still and always the best person I know.

'Fuck me,' she says, but weakly. And then: 'please.'

I push my lips wet into her shoulder, and she tastes unworldly. Some shameful instinct recoils at her sickness, but I hold my mouth pressed to her, clamping my eyelids and reciting the best things I know – where to stroke, squeeze, slap; where soft and where hard; to never, ever turn out the light – and I understand that too soon I'll know nothing worth knowing at all. So I wait for the pill.

Please.

'It's alright,' she says, 'I think they take a while to kick in. Just hold me.'

And I remember she is and always will be the stronger one.

The Last Dream

Julie Evans

It's a flat line. Not your heart. Your brain. Your heart pulses with the vigour of youth. Its signals are a false hope, she says. They are little earthquakes on a seismological screen.

I ask her if you dream. She shakes her head and her beeper sounds. Somebody else's crisis.

'I'll leave you to think,' she says. She touches my arm.

I think.

I think you need dreams, my love. Dreams are memories refracted through a prism. I lift each one of mine from some half-locked place inside me, carefully...carefully, and give them to you. My dreams are as fragile as gold leaf, and I am afraid they will quiver and fold as I carry them.

Take them. Hold them tight.

They are the silent pulses in your fontanelle.

They are ten miraculous fingers lost in uniform sleeves, knee-caps too big for your skinny legs.

They are the muddy grins for your first – and only – man of the match.

They are unspoken things – the graffiti scratched behind your bed, the cannabis plant dead behind the shed, a sock stuck in your printer, a condom in your wallet.

They are L-plates in the kitchen bin, a crunch of tyres on gravel, an engine roar fading into distance.

They are rows of As and a letter from Cambridge. You got in, by the way.

Here they all are, fluttering inside this one last precious dream. It's the one where you wake up... and you're you again.

Shedding

Jim Toal

Each night she comes to the alley and waits. Through a peephole scratched in the blackened windowpane, Abby can see her, the vixen, red fur sullied by the city's filth.

Vivienne: the name of her favourite soft toy as a little girl. Her brother, Dean, as a joke, once fed her to his pet snake. She bulged inside the snake's stomach as it curled up in its tank to digest. Later, the snake regurgitated Vivienne out, bedraggled and slimy. A strange, vinegary smell lingered in her fur long after she came out of the washing machine.

The vixen disappears behind bins to rummage for food, but returns and sits. Waits. She always does.

Voices outside the door.

She hurries from the window, flops on the narrow bed. In a corner, there's a small sink for washing. A yellow plastic bucket, underneath, for a toilet. Her body itches, her insides crawl. She bunches her stained nightie into a grey, featureless puppet poking from her fist. *Hello, Vivienne. How are you today?*

The door unlocks and opens. Still, there's that tiny burst of hope it might be Ashraf. His gorgeous smile. She would forgive him. Things could return to how they were. She still loves him.

She remembers the snake's shed skin. Twisted, a tattered fishnet stocking stripped from a thigh. Transparent and colourless. Delicate. Dry between her fingers.

Another stranger enters. The door locks behind him. He is old and moves slowly. His walking stick taps across the bare floorboards. Reaching the bed, he leans over her, puts his wrinkled face up close. Teases his tongue between his chapped lips and sniffs her skin like checking for milk on the turn.

He peels away her nightie, groans, and chucks it on the floor. Licks her neck, fumbles at his flies. While, unseen, her discarded nightie uncoils and slinks to the locked door. Her ghost. Free of her body, this world, it slips underneath. Slithers downstairs. Past men playing cards. Across the hall. Rears at the letterbox, silently slides through. Where, like every night, the vixen waits to take her in its soft, warm maw and return her to its den.

Immolation

Jacob Ian Decoursey

Becca and I had broken into a salvage yard and climbed atop the hood of a rusted Volkswagen. There was no reason, just something to do. She'd done this before. It was my first time. We lay looking up at the overcast night. Downhill, blacktop glittered like clusters of tiny fires beneath the orange glow of streetlamps, the prior rain having given way to a light fog. Cicadas screamed through the starless dark. The folding sounds of night enveloped us. I felt her fingers in my pocket.

'I'm cold.'

The night was cold, for early June.

I asked her, 'What now?'

She told me she didn't care.

'Do you want to have sex?'

'Not really,' she said and pushed her head into my jacket.

'Okay,' but then, 'how come?'

'I don't know.' She wrapped herself around me, pressed her groin into my leg and reached under my shirt.

'Okay,' I said.

Her fingers spidered up my chest and out the neck hole of my shirt. She looked up, smiled and touched my face, then pulled her hands out of my clothes and sat up.

Later, in her bedroom, I laid my jacket on her carpet and took my shoes off. She stripped to her underwear and lay in bed. To the left of the room, a window was open.

I walked to the bed, kissed her cheek, and whispered, 'I just want you to love me as much as I love you,' so quietly she wouldn't hear and tell me, 'I don't.'

She offered to let me sleep in bed with her, the way we had before.

I declined.

'Okay,' she said.

It started raining again. The Cicadas ceased. Droplets tapped against the windowsill. I thought about the clouds raining fire instead of water, about standing in the downpour and what it must look like being eaten by all the warm colors.

Twelve-Step
Jack Parker

It must have been one summer when I visited my Aunt and Uncle who lived on a farm in Ceredigion. Auntie loved me very much, but I reminded her too much of my father, especially as I got older, she said. She never understood why my father fought, but he always told me he was fighting for the greater good of his family. My Uncle was a very strict man, and he did not understand Auntie's affection for me. He told me that my mother should have gotten help with her 'habit' and this upset me very much.

Whenever he was in town attending the livestock auctions, Auntie let me out to explore. I used to go down the track through the woods to the beach, and I used to watch the fox fishing. I never wanted to tell anyone about him because no one would believe me, but the fox used to fish off the rocks like a bear. The fish got trapped in pools at low tide, and he'd trap the fish between his jaws. He often saw me watching him, but he didn't mind.

After supper they always drank a clear liquid. They seemed to love each other more when they drunk it. I got in the habit of drinking water after supper so that I could mix the alcoholic liquid into my water and they'd never know. One night I poured too much in, and I became dizzy, and I began to tell them about the fox. My Uncle became very angry and said I should have told him I'd seen a fox straight away. He asked me if I liked to have fresh eggs every day, so I told him I did like his eggs very much. I don't think he cared when I told him the fox only liked fish.

It always surprised me that the flies ate the eyes. I knew they'd lay larvae in the flesh around the gunshot wound, but I didn't expect them to eat the eyes. I think that was the first death I saw as a direct result of drinking.

Fox

Don Taylor

The cubs chew my paw: restless, hungry. My belly, too, is hollow.

The sun sinks behind the long barrow. Above the brook hangs the evening star.

Even here, wombed in the deep earth, scents come. I sniff and sort. Rabbit: a doe newly-kindled, the kits weak and blind. So, *good*. But *wait*, a pheasant (a hen), then faint... but clear: a bitch.

I lick the cubs; now only three, since the buzzard. My vixen noses me, her rough tongue pink on russet cheeks, flicks my coal-black snout; to stir courage; to coax. She too smells the bitch, rummaging the brackened woods, and perhaps a human, and with the human: a gun.

No. I don't get human. Yet.

I turn like a swirl of blood in a pool, slink along the den's gullet, stick my head into the bristling air. Sloe-black eyes drink in the light left to the world. The pale-blue sky. Studded stars glow-glimmer, expecting the dark. Fearful, tree-shadows lean from the silver moon creeping up the sky. An owl perched silent white upon the pine, harkens for vole-stir, scamper of mouse, twitch of toad, flaps once, and floats along the meadow. I face the breeze, the grass cool on my pads, ears-pricked for the drum of rabbit feet, nostrils flared for the stink of bitch and man.

Geese. One head swivels, honks, wings erupt skyward.

Head down, lick chops; dry still, not easy greasy with goose fat yet.

Skirt the meadow, keep the shadow, shun the moon's pale stare. Every trick, each sleight and feint. Pad, delicate upon dewy colts-foot, campion and oxslip.

My listening paw raised, cocked. Tail-twitch. The death-rustle, and *pounce!*

Fangs-fur-bone-blood-crack.

Man ghosts the wood-edge, slides one cartridge, red and gold, snug in each barrel. The dog's whimper.

'Back, Bess. Down.' Narrowed eyes scan the darkening. The bitch snuffs, ears twitch.

117

A spit of death-fire, a pop, a wreath of smoke. Fox-fur is a wet tatter, legs are rags.

YAP, YAP, YAP, YAP, YAP.

All creation is pain and barking.

Confectionery Cacophony

Danny Beusch

Her hand is sticky from the bribes she's taken. Vanilla ice cream, strawberry sauce, melted chocolate, candyfloss: gooey morsels that melt on her tongue, dance through her blood and, for just a moment, penetrate her shell.

Are you OK, sweetheart?

She's sick of adults and their incessant talking: barbed words that catch inside and rip you to shreds; flimsy words that float away on the slightest breeze. Five years old and she's had enough.

*

Sweets never featured in his plan. He'd imagined daisy-dotted picnics with carrot crudités, homemade hummus. Fresh fruit for pudding. Hugs and kisses. Lullabies. The social worker warned him: *our children are not like that.* He nodded, made the right noises: *of course, of course.*

*

Screams float into the funhouse from the outside rides, making her jump. *Another bad idea*, he mutters, under his breath. She walks ahead to the end of the narrow corridor, never looking back, and into the hall of mirrors.

He finds her staring. The red tick scarring her left cheek, the drugged-up rage of a sofa-surfing uncle, has folded upon itself and vanished. Her arms and legs, stick-thin and stunted by neglect, have stretched to superhuman size. Even her lips curve upwards. A ripple. A crescent. An almost-smile.

It's magic, he says.

She licks her fingers, finds a sherbet anaesthetic, and climbs the stairs to the next level. Gazing at his lonely, distorted reflection he has an idea.

*

Doughnut grease seeps through the paper in blotches. They devour four each before he tips up the bag and opens his throat to cascading clumps of sugar.

Black clouds gather, thunder rolls, revellers scatter to find shelter. The first droplets land on his fingertips with a fizz and tingle.

She grabs his leg, gripping tight, as their bodies melt, granule-by-granule, into a viscous pool of syrup. Giddy with anticipation, they wait – as the surging water mixes, thins, dilutes – sending them flowing, together, as one: a giddy sugar-rush over concrete, amongst blades of grass, through soil, down to where words cannot reach.

Ballad of the Drowned Canary

Lucy Grace

It is an addiction, the piano. The mahogany case smells salty damp, the soundboard keening for the sea. Shaved razor-thin whale lung cavity, ribbed with bird bones, otherworldly. Her manager has stopped emailing – next week when it is six months since, her pay will cease entirely, but she will not notice. Eva is absorbing sea fret like the soaking wood, glints of brass shine in her eyes, wedded to the gilded key around her neck.

The piano sits in this high-ceilinged fireplace room, lost and left by previous tenants before they were ended. Each day Eva looks in the mirror and gifts herself a silent day, a day of recovery, yet even before commuters reach their desks she is settled on the stool, thin fingers rested on wasting thighs, unlit sunlit skin drying and ageing.

And the phone stops ringing, and the letterbox spits bills onto bills.

On the floor of a cage near the window, the skeleton of a small bird diminishes and desiccates. Once bright ivory, it swallowed the notes that killed it. Its feathers now fold faded, bare bleached by uncurtained summer glare.

Still, she plays. The upstairs neighbours are listening, unhearing, the music as constant as the sun.

Still, the sounds flicked onto the papery staves are bleeding and blotted: black blood, spattered from a cut vein.

Still, she strokes the keys tenderly, encouragingly, lingering on warmed enamel, hurrying over narrow black gaps.

Still, she nets only minor refrains.

There is no longer any family. Her friends all died in the mines. The flat and the piano and the palely lit corpse bird are all that she was. Now she is almost selkie gone. Her skin yellows, salted and swollen, splitting and plum-bursting with the sea stench of a sunken man.

Still, she plays. Melancholy melodies as wretched as the grey days she has left, until the new tenants come with their coffee ma-

chine and wireless Alexa and place smiling photo frames on the piano, and she is no longer apparent to anyone.

Still, here, the piano.

Star Cross'd

Conor Montague

We traipse in silence through damp fragrant Bloomsbury streets. Magnolia petals strewn about sopping paths glisten like moonlit lilies upon long contemplative ponds. 'The mansion of the Earl stood at the far end of the square,' I venture, 'replaced by that grandiose monument to grand larceny.' You smirk at my feigned outrage, grasp my hand and lead me onto stepping-stones of patrons and sonnets, dark ladies and platonic love.

Poached eggs and toast in a bright all-night diner. We chat as if there'll be other evenings, long walks into the future, lazy recollections of the past we would share. Sip the pretence with our tea, fortified by its warmth. I tip the sarcastic Irish waiter – gratuity for his walk-on role – and trail your rich cinnamon bouquet into the rain.

Black cab trundles through pothole, drenches the tartan drainpipes of a screen-swiping hipster. Your giggle gurgles through manic bustle as the hipster spits fire at the heavens. Surge of blind brollies sweep me before a clanging rickshaw. I spring back and parry with matador flourish, strike pose as it clatters past.

I turn to you gone. A bus shoulders its way into traffic. Your silhouette through misted pane evokes the Monet we viewed earlier. Your Gallic lilt introducing *Le Bateau-atelier*. Your absence as you gazed upon the scene. The delicate blush of its mournful sky.

Following My Best Friend's Mother into the Ocean

Christopher X. Ryan

At the water's edge she brings her hands together as if about to shadow-puppet a bird, arches over the surf, and disappears into a whitecapped wave.

I follow, wading into a sea swollen with kelp the color of dried blood. When I reach her, I lay a strand on her neck. She throws it at me. I catch it, then don it like a wilted crown.

Soon the bottom drifts away. Treading, we look back at the fathers, brothers, and other mothers, now just shimmers in the late-summer light.

'Babies,' she says. 'Come on, let's race to the slide.'

She's halfway there before I've even escaped the undertow. I claw at the waves, but when I take in a mouthful and lose my grip on the surface, I have no choice but to sink, then propel myself off the conch-riddled bottom. Surfacing, I flail for the splintery gray ladder.

I ascend, then collapse on the warped planks beside her. The clouds merge overhead.

She laughs. 'Are you OK?'

I nod, shuddering, though I'm not cold. The clouds separate.

We lie still a long while until she says, 'OK, let's do it.'

She hauls up the tethered bucket and christens the slide.

'You first.'

I shrug, then curve into the dock's cold and eclipsed underbelly. At the bottom, though, I wait for her, and she glides into my embrace.

I bring my face toward hers.

'No,' she says, cupping my mouth. 'We're just swimming.'

We tread again, the waves herding us back to shore.

'I can't start a new life,' she says, then swims away.

She sticks close to the dock, weaving in and out of the barnacled pilings – until a wave pummels her, subsumes her. I spot a curled hand rising through the gray-green foam and swim for it.

I haul her up by the roots of her hair.

Fathers and sons pull us out, then kneel beside us in the sand. My best friend's mother is heaving, her legs quivering, her eyes searching for the light.

'What happened?' they ask.

'Something attacked us,' I say.

'What was it?'

'Not sure,' I say.

'Just some creature,' she says.

The Water-Carrier

Charlotte Newman

She hates the vase. All day long she carries it. She is transport, first and foremost; a vehicle for a receptacle.

It looks like brass – of the kind you might find in a market. To the inexperienced eye it could as easily be a relic as a model. She can never put it down, only empty it into that great tidal river that snakes through the city. The vase will refill immediately with the post-midnight blues.

To what end she performs this task, she can't say. Not because it's secret, but because she doesn't know. She only knows that the vase is hers, and so is the labour that comes with it. The strain has made lines on her young forehead, even incurred a tremble in her wrists. The point is, you can't just put down the tears of a diasporic city.

Her gaze on the street, she walks.

Spilling is a constant fear, magnified by night's approach – fighting, touching; lunar action can knock a person off-balance. It doesn't bear thinking about, all that salt-raw grief upturned on London. It doesn't bear thinking about, but she will. She tightens her grip. Sometimes a whole day goes by before she realises her hands are clawed.

It's only 5 P.M., and the vase is tipping full.

It carries Mrs Walker's sorrow for her cat Sid (and late husband of the same name). It carries the pearls of a Lambeth new-born. There are first-years in town missing their country mothers; two-for-one shots become two-for-one tears and sit in the vase like oil. Very few drops belong to those without homes. They have had to learn to ration.

There's a prickle at her own eyes. *Stop*, she thinks.

She mustn't add to the vase.

It may be small, but it's heavy.

Consuelo

Bruce Meyer

A man in the bus station stood staring into the black screen of his dead cell phone as he shouted her name as if he had been wounded and was suffering from a great pain. He shouted it as if he was falling to his knees in the rain and begging forgiveness or pleading for a second chance.

But what caught my attention was a kid whom I couldn't see who was seated on the banquette behind me and who kept pacing up and down, talking in a noticeable New York-Queens accent about how there weren't any girls in this town and he was coming back to New York because he'd left all his gaming equipment in his old room and he didn't want the person on the other end of the conversation to pitch it out if he didn't return.

And as I looked around the bus station where mothers usually waited late at night with their sleeping children on the seats beside them, or college girls stared at their laptops and chewed gum while listening to their playlists through umbilical earbuds, or old women in headscarves sat nervously on the edge of their seats, clutching at their black shoulder bags because the sound of revving bus engines reminded them of being deported at gunpoint when they were children, I looked up, and all the women were gone.

I waited ten, fifteen minutes or more because my bus wouldn't be leaving for another hour in the middle of the night, and not a single woman appeared. There were only men, some of them old, some of them young, sitting, staring straight ahead, and empty-eyed as if they had all been struck dumb in disbelief. They didn't speak amongst themselves. I couldn't speak to them. I had nothing to say. And the kid from New York who kept asking someone on the other end of the cell phone call if they were there, repeated 'Hello? Hello?' and slapped the phone in the palm of his hand several times as if it wasn't working. And the man with the dead cell phone and blackened screen who had called out for Consuelo, leaned against a pillar and wept over what, he told me, he couldn't remember about the light he had known in her eyes.

Directional Projections
Anita Goveas

We lie on the roof of your spring onion green Toyota, in the usual place beside the oak trees just hidden from the entrance to the park, and ask ourselves the big questions.

What does a beam of light long for, you say, twisting the cap off your peach iced tea with a fluid motion that makes your bangles chime, an energy that radiates down my spine. The air turns perfumed, sugary.

It longs for distance and the flow through space, we decide, smiling at beams impatient at planets getting in the way.

What do the stars taste of, I murmur, hoping to match your perpendicular way of looking at the world, swallowing into a dry mouth. You'll be off to study the stars soon, I'll stay here, turn seeds into oak trees. Some things take time.

That's easy you say, tipping the bottle up so your lips don't touch it, passing it to me. Nothing, hydrogen, helium, everyone knows they're tasteless. I'm lying too flat to take a drink, pass the bottle straight back.

I want to say, a beam of light has no friends, it finds its own path. If there's an obstacle, it goes through it. It's about the journey it says, not about the end. No-one enjoys being the obstacle.

What makes a beam of light scatter, you say, finishing off the bottle with a long deep glug. Sucking up every tiny drop.

That's easy, I say. Time. And obstacles.

Now

Andrew Miller

'If it's political art, I'm just not interested,' she says, defiant, confident. 'Seriously. There's a limit. I know it's awful, but I no longer care.'

He nods seriously, fast, all eyes and focus. 'Absolutely. No question.'

'Which might make me sound like a callous upper-class bitch...'

'I'm down with bitches,' he laughs and tosses the whiskey back. 'So, we gonna do this?'

Her name is Cynthia, and she forces them to say it. Preferably to scream it, but at least to form it on their tongues and get it out into the air. At least. Just once. It's a personal philosophy – she thinks it means they'll probably remember her in some way, short term at least.

She doesn't bother with their names. And yes, she knows. But it's never been her thing. Irony.

His name is Asani, and he doesn't care who knows it, or remembers it, or says it. He's Nigerian, half new to the city, and bored. The white ladies have certain desires, and he's dying for something, anything, so... they end up at a hotel, medium range, nothing dirty, but no one's spending too much either. They'll split the bill. Which hasn't been discussed, but they both know.

As far as Tinder goes, it's about a 6.5, so not too bad. Both have had worse. Cynthia, in fact, is coming off a string of 2s and 3s, so there are moments she feels elevated, rushing, semi-ecstatic. Asani vibes on this and gets a bit theatrical, feels the moment, and the next. And then they're putting on their shoes and it's quiet and the smell has changed and the carpeting is especially thin at the foot of the bed, which they both notice, and which sets each of them adrift on their own, personal rafts.

'Well, Cynthia,' he says as they diverge in the foyer, still twinkling a bit at the name thing. 'It's been fun. Thank you.'

'No, thank you!' she gives him a wide, cover-all, name-forgetting smile.

They touch fingers as they move away and it's almost like a handshake – a first, flickering, cautious hello.

Fight Fair

Kristina Ten

He brought his pitchfork to the conversation, and she brought her ladle. There is something between them that requires excavation, the uncovering of, the pulling up of – neither of them knows what, exactly, but knows they'll know when they find it.

His pitchfork is old and rust-covered and comprised almost entirely of points. He hasn't used it before, but he has seen pictures, thinks he can figure it out well enough. His pitchfork is too big for him. Maybe he thought they would hold it together, grips alternating on the long handle, synchronized pushing into the hard ground.

Maybe he didn't think she would bring the ladle.

Her ladle is small with a deep, round basin. It is gilded, and the curve of the handle fits only two of her fingers and pinches those painfully, and she was never under the impression that there would be room enough for him too.

They dig together. They take turns so it feels equal, but as they go, the pile of dirt on his side grows so much taller than the pile on hers.

He throws his body at the pitchfork. It brings up large clots and knocks holes in pipes; it mutilates the earth. She dips the ladle carefully, each turn taking only as much as the basin can hold, the dirt perfectly level with the metal edge, no heaps or hills, her progress slower than slow.

She doesn't ask why he brought the pitchfork, and he doesn't make mention of her ladle. It's only when their hands are blistered and blood-slick, their brows drenched from the effort, that they remember the shovel they keep in the shed.

Tamagotchi Blues

Andrew Boulton

Archie's electric dog died, so we had a funeral. It was the sort of shitty off-brand toy dad always bought us so when it stopped working, and Archie tried to open the back with a butter knife, it started smoking. Of course it did.

Now we're at Grandad's because he has a garden and he says we can dig a small – 'do you hear me, boys, *small*' – hole if I promise to mow both of his lawns till I go back to school.

Archie has wrapped the electric dog in an Indiana Jones pillowcase that Dad had accidentally burned with his cigarette, right through the dot of the 'I' in the word 'Raiders'.

But Grandad tells us to stop digging pretty much right away, and that means the hole isn't big enough for the dog and the pillowcase. I should say something to Grandad, but I know he's going to be digging up the electric dog and putting it in the bin as soon as we've left.

So I take off my sock, and I tell Archie to wrap the dog in that. And now it does fit, and we put the electric dog in the hole and cover it over, and Archie tries to sing one of the songs Mum used to sing to him, but he's forgotten most of the words.

Then it starts to rain and we go. Archie's not crying and not even trying not to cry. And me, still wearing one sock, is trying to remember the last time he did.

Only Eight Is Everything

Tom O'Brien

The red numbers of the digital clock are all the boy can see. 0759.

I can't get up, he says. Loud but in his head. Can't get up. Can't.

The red glow is the only thing in the womb black room. Lined curtains help him sleep when he can. No light seeps around the memory of a door.

The clock could be huge and far away, could be small and near. He knows where it is. Beyond arm's reach, so he has to move to switch off the alarm.

The boy smells toast from downstairs. Faint, like the memory of toast.

0759 turns to 0800.

There is no alarm.

The boy looks at the three zeroes, the single eight. Puzzled.

The alarm should shrill at 0800 whether or not he sets it. There is no forgetting.

An illicit idea thrills him. If it doesn't sound he can stay in this timeless place.

The boy stares at the numbers that loom over him like light pillars of a future city. Or his room is spinning, adrift in time, leaving him breathless and dizzy as he lies there.

The numbers glow, and their unused shapes glow less. Hexagons. Who taught him that?

Only 8 uses every piece. But seven stretched hexagons make the 8. Tiny lozenge sweets. Headstones. That doesn't seem right. It should be eight pieces? His face never leaves the pillow, but the thought spins him.

0801. Two whole but incomplete 0's. The 8 that uses everything. And now 1, which uses least of all. Stacked hexagons, tip to tip, balanced.

The alarm stopped. It had been buzzing for sixty seconds. The ragged metallic taste in his mouth tells him he has been screaming to drown it. The true silence confirms it.

Downstairs, the boy sees the bowl with the spoon in it, the cereal box moved enough to show his father thought of him. There will be fresh milk in the fridge, but there is no toast.

The smell was a memory. His mother is a memory.

The 8 uses seven pieces because that's all there are, but it becomes 0 when one piece is missing.

An Ocean Swims Above Our Heads
Santino Prinzi

We're not underwater, we're *under*water. My husband tells me this is the effect the aquarium is going for like I hadn't reached that conclusion myself. This is what he wants me to believe. He wants me to believe this is the same as scuba diving, only safer. He's a cheapskate. This shouldn't be a problem, but it is.

I'm walking through a finger-marked glass tube with too many people breathing. I can smell clammy skin, I can see body heat lingering on rustling coats. Inauthentic aquatic sounds are pumped through tinny speakers. We're all under: under water, under a spell, underwhelmed.

He holds my hand because he believes I'll wander off. That or he loves me. He's pulling my arm, wanting to get through the aquarium quickly. I resist and take my time. If I can't go diving, then I'm getting every pennyworth.

He feigns enthusiasm and points at a stingray. *That Irwin fella*, he says. I only smile because the stingray is itself beautiful, carving itself through invisible streams like a graceful bird.

Tropical fish shimmer through rocks and plants. They must miss their home, assuming they know any different. Perhaps it's kinder if they don't know what it's like swimming among coral reefs, dodging plastic bottles and the like. You can't miss what you've never had, but somehow, really, you can. You can miss everything.

People huff. I'm committing a cardinal sin of the modern era: I'm standing still in a public place. But I don't want to move. I close my eyes and pretend I'm submerged, that there's no sweaty groups of school children clambering at the glass tube walls.

My husband squeezes my hand. I could let go. He could swim the oceans' depth while I barnacle myself here. He squeezes my hand again, firmer this time. It means, *I love you*, or, *Get a move on*. I don't open my eyes to check which it is.

Stillness

Ruth Davies

On my drive home from work – only 60 kilometres, which I can do in half an hour at an average speed of 120 kmph, which is possible when there's no speed limit on the sealed road and there's only 10 kilometres of dirt road and I spend a good chunk of the time on the sealed road doing 140, 150 clicks an hour willing something, a kangaroo, a pig, to come out in front of me – there's a hill that rises steeply and roundly from a perfect plain. It's covered so evenly in bushes that from here it looks smooth. I call it Marble Hill. Every day, I look across the field of para grass growing around Marble Hill, and I think, 'I'm going to stop the car. I'm going to get out. I'm going to walk through that scrub, up that hill and sit at the top, screened by those bushes, and I'm never coming down.'

At home, he's usually on his third beer by the time I get inside. He's only been home half an hour himself, but he says he drinks so much because it's so hot. Before we lived in the tropics, he said he drank because he needed to keep warm. The TV is always blasting so it can be heard over the air-conditioning, right through dinner, a stream of news and sport. In the wet season the house smells of his working day, of his beer, of his feet. Most days I leave his socks where he's dropped them on the living room floor, but sometimes I get over myself and pick them up deliberately and gingerly by the dry end and carry them down to the laundry without a word.

One day I come in the house, and he's not there. His car has gone, his suitcase has gone. Did he have travel booked? There is only the stale smell of a house closed up, musty already in the still, humid air. The walls press in.

Chemistry

Raj Bahia

He set to work again. Good steady hands. That was vital. It was tricky business. Fiddly. Don't want to make any mistakes. The parts can be small, and you don't want to lose any. I remember those hands around my waist all those years ago. They were steady then too, always knew how to touch all the right places.

Fifteen years, how we'd grown. Two intertwined souls connecting through intertwined bodies.

He got the beaker, held the light underneath it. He'd graduated in Physics, but I always thought Chemistry was more his forte. Chemistry that brought us together, chemistry that keeps us together. My clever, handsome man. My saviour, because he is much better at the jobs than me. It's good to have a man who can cook. Always offering me first servings too.

'It tastes a bit like plastic,' I said.

'Yeah, maybe. Industrial.'

'Mmmm whatever it is, I like it.'

His fingers, I know them so well now. So many times I'd eagerly watch him at work. Getting things ready for us. The fingers that curl with mine as we lay in bed, exhausted yet wide awake. Jittery, sometimes paranoid but mostly happy.

First we were addicted to the sex, then the love. Then the music. The poetry, the night ramblings about Bukowski and Rimbaud.

And finally the crack cocaine.

This is where we settled. There was nothing further we were interested in getting ourselves obsessed with. We reached a plateau. And the plateau felt good. Insatiable even. We had no need to acquire anything new.

And so together we inhale and exhale, and we still ramble about the poets whilst we listen to the music, and we still sleep intertwined. Fingers, hands and legs. Everything's the same, but nothing remains. We're no longer a slave to the love, we're a slave to the drug.

And together we convince ourselves of the beauty of our fate, as we inhale and exhale and inhale...

When We Were Vietnamese

Nicky Kippax

They came here on a boat. We told people just as we'd overheard it – but we didn't know anything.

I was nine, and you seven.

For a while we lived in their flat upstairs: jabbing at polystyrene squares they glued to the walls, sharing boiled rice dipped from a sack into palm-size bowls and taking our turn nodding to 'grand-mother' on top of the fridge, beset with plastic flowers and smoking sticks.

Our friend, their daughter – long-limbed and brown-skinned – with a curtain of black hair hiding her eyes. Always graceful in her forest green school uniform and pulled socks.

We celebrated New Year twice – again with our adopted Viet-namese family in January. We ate sticky buns filled with sweetmeats and were each given a shiny twenty pence piece because they were new back then. Dragons danced on the heads of men – forked tongues ablaze with streamers – and our patent shoes marked the community hall floor as we gladly became their tail.

On the way home you knelt on an upturned nail. My friend's fa-ther panicked; we couldn't understand his words. He lifted you and ran through the streets – his white celebration shirt turning slowly red.

That night you stayed in hospital for the first time ever. It was the same night that our mum asked us to stop being Vietnamese.

Twenty years later I visited Vietnam and saw photographs of families who were later lost to the waves from stricken fishing boats. In one picture I saw a father lifting his child to shore – small body coddled inside his white shirt – his face grimly set against the waves.

I decided that actually, we will always be a little bit Vietnamese.

Matricide

Mariam Varsimashvili

Any history of depression in the family?

I think of the grandmother who jumped. I imagine she was like a stone, intending to skip on the water but designed to sink down.

I only know her from a sepia photograph in which she wears a white dress and outshines the two men standing to the left of her in black suits. They are photographed on a bridge over a river. I search the picture for potential hints of her intention.

I ask my mother if it is *the* bridge but get no response. At the hospital, I try to deflect the doctor's questions. I provide her with minor information like how I rubbed an orange peel on my temples and wrists, hoping it would overpower the stench of rotting flesh.

It is my mother that is rotting. She left eight chicken thighs to defrost in the sink and never came back for them. The chicken attracted a horde of flies. I bought pesticide, sprayed them one by one and waited upstairs, giving them privacy to die.

Her room has been transformed into a large medicine cabinet. I often familiarise myself with the names of her pills, as if pronouncing them correctly in a row will activate their potential of changing the chemical flow in my mother's brain. *Citalopram, Fluoxetine, Sertraline, Paroxetine.* She calls them receptor antagonists.

At night, I sneak into her medicine cabinet and snuggle on her pillow that's littered with black strands of greasy hairs.

My rotting mother is making the walls in our house damp. Everything in the house copies her; spiders dangle from old cobwebs like cheap Halloween decoration. They have nothing to feed on because I murdered their prey.

How often have you been bothered by worrying?

I often think of the grandmother who jumped.

Woman troubles. Grief. Laziness. Bad company. Self-abuse. Desertion by husband.

How often have you been bothered by feeling that you have let yourself and your family down?

Soon I will have to cut her loose, like chicken from the fat.

The Wind

Lauren Everdell

She used to think she hated the wind. The way the sound of it scoured the back of her mind like sand as she tried to dream. Filling her sleep with sighing. Shifting the tide of her blood until it slopped and foamed like sea spume inside her.

She should have known it for the premonition it was.

That way she'd have been prepared.

But instead she became a stranger to her body when it happened. Her health draining like water through a crack in a bowl.

She imagined it leaving her: seeking out someone better. Someone who'd make something with it. Someone worthy, as she had apparently not been.

She wondered who.

Until one day she understood Hope had abandoned her too: clasping hands with Health, unnoticed, as they fled away. And the future, once a rainbow city on the horizon, became a scouring wind of its own. Filled with sand the colour of bone.

And, eventually, a voice.

A whisper, then a sigh. Then a song.

When it became a scream, she followed it. Away from home and up, through bowing trees that shed leaves like the tears she had never cried. With path stones pressing through the soles of her shoes, and the voice like a grey thread she ran through her fingers. As Theseus had once, in his labyrinth.

Until she came to a hill of thrashing grass under bruised and bleeding sunset sky.

Higher than everything around her. Higher than the tops of the trees that cried on her behalf. And there she rooted herself.

The wind licked the salt sweat from her skin. Devoured her words as she cried out that she was there; it had told her to come, and she was there.

When she raised her arm into it, she wasn't surprised that the wind began to bite at her. That her skin began to flake away like ancient paint dried by the sun. She watched herself dissolve into the air, drifting as dandelion seeds do. Grateful, relieved, with a feeling like going home.

All the Sky Above Us
Christopher M Drew

I launch my four-year-old son into the air and he laughs because he knows I will catch him.

He climbs on my shoulders and his long fingernails claw at my neck. Daddy, he says. Play Monster.

At the forest boundary I lift him over the stile, turn around, and count to ten. After ten the Monster will come.

One, two, three, I say.

A sharp wind carves through the field and flattens the tall grass.

Four, five, six.

Close by, a herd of cattle shelters near the foaming mouth of the river.

Seven, eight.

Beside me is a coppiced oak with its limbs stripped bare. A ravaged nest sways high in the branches. At the foot of the tree is a broken egg. A tiny chick lies wet and pink amongst the fragments.

Nine, ten, I say. The Monster is here.

Along the forest trail a man walks with a stout bulldog. The man kneels and unhitches a chain from the dog's collar. He throws a stick into the river and the dog lunges through the shallow water. On tiptoe my son peers over the bridge and the stick floats beneath him.

The man screams the dog's name and my son screams Daddy.

I vault over the stile and the dog cuts through the water.

I'm here, I say. Don't move.

A sharp whistle slices the air but the bulldog snarls and tears up the riverbank.

My son backs away and trips over the wooden boards in his rubber boots.

Daddy, he says.

The bulldog charges across the bridge and then leaps.

I'm right here, I say.

My son reaches out and his hood snaps back. Rain soaks his dark red hair.

Overhead, the treetops groan in the wind and peel back until there is nothing above us but sky.

Unseen Dangers

Lauren Collett

The car lurches around another corner, and she is relieved, once again, to see nothing coming towards them. Her fingers are firmly weaved together on her lap, in order to keep herself in check. He has never crashed, she reminds herself. The problem is that he is easy-going, and she is not. It is her father's voice that she hears in her head, from those ten-to-two lessons, twenty years ago; *blind corners, hedged stone walls, unseen dangers.*

He accelerates again, so she holds her breath. Imperceptibly, of course; she has learnt the importance of that. Last year, driving from Florence airport down to Tuscany, she'd annoyed him so much with her gasping, her flinching, her nagging, that he'd ended up pulling over. He couldn't bear it anymore. She'd driven the rest of the way, white-knuckled and clammy on the steering wheel, wide-eyed behind her sunglasses. From the passenger seat, he had light-ened the mood, reading out hopeful listings from the internet: *Ten places to visit on your Tuscan honeymoon!*

She knows that she is lucky. He always tries to make the best of it, no matter what she does to ruin things. And he can make her laugh; that's what you want from a marriage, isn't it? Laughter. A sense of humour, even when they see the worst of you.

She's thinner now; her wedding ring, once snug, trembles over each bump in the road. She adjusts her grasp upon herself, gripping the ring between two fingers. Happily, her thumb is now free to dig into the top of her hand. She pins herself down. Breathes out.

He knows; of course he knows. But knowing isn't enough. A quick glance reveals the whites of her knuckles glowing like tiny moons in her lap. She is folded into herself, like perfect origami. She is a neatly gutted fish. He thinks of her bones, licked clean. He hard-ens, and slows the car, looking for somewhere to park.

The Crow

Laura Warminger

This is the first time we have met in this room, me and the crow. We smile and attempt light conversation, twittering about the weather and what the children have been learning at school. The room is small, although I never noticed this before. Like a nest it is lined with the twigs and leaves of a life now passed. The favourite chair bestrew with papers, the water bill and two copies of *That's Life*. There is a note for the milkman under the blue cup with the chipped handle, lipstick marking the shape of her mouth.

The crow ruffles her feathers to signal she is done with the niceties and wants to get on. I suggest we begin with the papers; the crow pretends she hasn't heard and swoops to a drawer in the sideboard. I watch as she picks through its contents, beady eyes searching through bits of string, paper clips and clothes pegs. Disappointed, the crow moves on to another and is rewarded with our mother's jewellery box. Feathers bristle with excitement, clawing at the catch until it reveals its treasures. The crow would like to take these, to remember her at her best. My memory is blackened by the nights spent holding hands whilst a frail body writhed and panted.

The crow has collated the best of the sideboard drawer and is googling their worth whilst updating its status on social media to grieving. We are fully-fledged opposites. Is there anything I would like to have, the creature wonders. I reassure it that there is nothing of note in the drawers, picking up the blue cup and the message for the milkman instead. The crow cackles to signal its amusement; I am just like our mother it tells me.

I shake my head, biting down hard on my tongue until I taste blood, the deep burning of resentment is scraping at my insides. It tears at my flesh and picks at the bones until they are clean. The thought of it makes me sob silent tears, this unsettles the crow, and it escapes through the open door.

The Chicken

Jeffrey David Montanye

She sets up the easel to paint the chicken, but the bird doesn't co-operate. It's just a lowly poultry bird, white with yellow feet, and a bright red comb and wattle, quite an ugly thing. With weak eyes, it runs behind the barn to find a hiding place under a thicket of burdocks. But the light is just right, and tomorrow the dinner bell rings, so she must gather him now before the sun goes down. The bird flits and flutters, beating its wings as she hauls it to the perch. Little chicks dart in all directions, they are far cuter and much easier to catch, but this one's dawn has come. For life is fleeting, but art is forever, in the halls of the great museums. The bird runs again, no interest in remembering, no desire to be immortalized. It's too late; the sun has set. Father comes with the ax. She sits before an empty canvas as the bird's last squawk echoes in the distance. Holding the paintbrush in her hand, she remembers the happy days, when the chicken she named Fred would dance for her in the yard. Moving the brush from memory, she paints what she can feel; a beautiful bird of rainbow colors and eyes as strong as steel.

Before the Baby Was Born

Hannah Storm

Do you remember how you told me you'd drown our child if he was born with red hair like mine? You wanted a son, dark-crowned, a mirror of your own. You, who believed nothing that others told you, followed all the old wives' tales for this new wife of yours, who you only wed because in this new Millennium you did not want a bastard baby. Curries and walks and all the teas and tinctures that might bring on labour. And sex because, didn't I know, you told me with all the coldness of a clinician eyeing his experiment, that semen ripened the cervix. It was in one of those fucking pub quizzes you hated that I finally let go to my body's natural rhythms, but only after I had proven to you that I knew more than you thought. If the contractions hadn't been so intense, we might have been first in the quiz not second. Still, I believed another prize was mine: this child born ten days late, thirty hours after labour began, six hours after we made it to the hospital, twenty minutes after I wallowed into the water. A girl who defied the scan, with hair so black I only knew she was mine because of how she came to be. You took her away before I had given up the afterbirth, puffed up with the pride of your achievement and offered her a stay of execution, but not me. While I lay wasted but for the great clots I bled, you announced you were hungry and wanted to go home, but not before I took her from you, clamped her to my empty breast, a lion mother born.

Sinker (a Dark Cadence)

Gary Budden

You were talking about the past and the things we had done before we knew what to do. I recalled how the sun died tired in our back garden, green that stretched out like a landing strip towards the cemetery. Over the wooden fence was where the dead lived and dreamed their dreams of London, trodden on by crackheads and alkies and the men seeking sex from men like themselves. I felt the slower we went the better, easy-does-it over the fence boys, but a night of heavy drinking had impaired an already stiff and unagile body. When I fell into the realm of the dead, my brittle collarbone snapped on a ruined grave, and my head poured crimson from its left side. I blacked out, and when I came to, had lost my filter and spoke openly of the things that preoccupied me, but I felt too embarrassed to express in daylight. This troubled you, who ushered me through the dank and dripping tombs to the exit, where we had summoned a flashing ambulance. A man from the council was summoned to unlock the Victorian gates; all present advised that trying to scale the boundaries of the necropolis a second time was foolish. The paramedics took my heartbeat, asked if I'd taken something, my chest thudding fast and hard; the irony was that that night, I hadn't.

All I could think about was that night in the cemetery; the mossed statues didn't make for easy conversation. What we failed to speak of was how we got ourselves through the dark days and made it all make sense; how we tried to stop ourselves sinking.

Float

David Hartley

She climbed onto the float, got her balance, and made her announcement to the pool. Only a few heard it. The lifeguards, of course, who blinked from their daydreams, and the giggly teens in the shallow end. She waited, knees wobbling, until swimmers stopped mid-stroke to stare, until goggles were lifted and dive-bombs were hesitated. She announced it again; louder, prouder. Water dripped a rhythm from her fingers to the float. She said it once more, for those at the back.

The settling wakes of swimmers rocked beneath her. She hadn't known it was possible to balance on a float, didn't know they could hold a person's weight. She dared not move. She didn't want to fall back in until they'd decided.

Applause. She grinned. She blushed. Two breaststrokers glided over and steadied her platform, one of the teens asked her to say it again, so she did. Whoops and cheers, clapping which became splashing. The dive-bomber jumped for joy and plunged.

The lifeguards blew up inflatables and pushed them out. The front-crawlers unhooked the ropes and lashed together a throne of squeaky plastics, a palace of air. They asked for her life story, and she told it. They asked for more, so she embellished, performed. The pool filled when word got out, a queue formed; she told fortunes.

But as sudden as it started, her time was done. She popped the valves and let the escaping air flop her back to the waters. Only a few acolytes remained. She gave them a rubber ring each, to remember her by. She pushed her weary legs to the ladder and climbed out. She showered, got her belongings from the locker, and when she reached the doors to the changing room, he turned left.

Watching the Homed

Dave O'Leary

I had a rusting pickup truck with a camper in the bed, and that was about it, and I parked in a quiet and clean neighborhood away from the others like me, the others without homes.

And I would sit there in the camper and watch the couple in the apartment across the street because I had no TV and they left their blinds open while they watched theirs.

And while staring at the corner where the TV was, they also looked at their phones, but they didn't talk much, and they probably thought they knew things about life.

But I doubted they ever wanted for much or not much that mattered anyway. It wasn't like they hadn't eaten for two days. Or was it three?

And when it snowed on a Saturday, I saw them carefully walk down the street and then carefully back not long after carrying a twelve-pack and a couple bottles of wine.

And they paused for a moment, looked in my direction with arms full of booze and perhaps wondered briefly what to do about the man in the camper parked on their street.

But I knew they could not see me in there and maybe they wanted it that way.

And that was fine, so I toasted to them with a shot of Old Grand-Dad which I'd nicked from the store down the street where they probably bought their own beverages.

And later I saw them in their apartment drinking and watching TV and staying warm as the warmth of the shot slowly and then quickly left me and my camper and then became something I no longer had.

And I considered then the impossible act of knocking on their door and asking for a drink or even just the slightest bit of warmth.

But then for the first time, they closed their blinds, and I could no longer see them, nor they my camper and I sat in the cold waiting for the only thing yet to come.

Making Chutney

Caroline Robinson

I hold summer close: count jars of jewelled jam, listen to the blips of fermenting wine as I stir surpluses into chutneys.

By morning the condensation will be solid stars, blotched across the caravan's panes. I'll haul my clothes under the covers to dress, displacing cats – the extra hour I could have lost – forgotten.

Tomorrow I'll pick my ram: Callum: huge, but gentle as a lamb – just as well. Maybe Sherman: pedigree as long as last wet winter's, but crazy as Mad Jock without a drink. Camus – possibly: beautiful as thistledown, but mental too. His blue-grey cloud of dense fleece like bonfire-smoke, horns curled thrice around, points tilted to hip height. I'll never turn my back to him but face him up – look straight into his slitty eyes.

Then I'll remember Spring: sharp nights trampling crisp fields, creatures rustling off into tall reeds, luminescent eyes glowing in the wide arc of my torchlight and the chilling bark of impatient foxes. Hot limp lambs, steaming out onto frozen grass, ewe's nostrils smoking in the black air and the sweet smell of brand-new life – hopefully.

All this time I've lived through seasons by the thought of the next. Planned ahead. Planted seeds that would take me three turns of the calendar to pick.

The phone rings. I lay the spoon across the top of the pan, rub my hands on my jeans.

My brother's dead. An overdose. There's to be a post-mortem – an enquiry… could be weeks before a funeral.

I rub my hand down the window, wipe it on my leg, stare out at the only light – my neighbours. Burning smells haul me back from past places. I have to go – rescue the chutney, bottle and label it for next season.

Welcome to the Sunshine State

CS Bowerman

As the I4 crosses the bridges in Florida, it sings. Every few miles the voice of the road changes, here shouting secrets, there crooning daydreams. It thinks we have forgotten the old songs that are now just grated through its lonesome concrete voicebox.

The harmonious water features, flat landscape and lakes are just scratches on a terrain that was once wild and impassable. The alligators are penned outside now behind meshlink warnings and spurious ditches, but freedom still lives in their primeval memories. They still hum with delicious fantasies of the Paleo-Indians who hide too well now to supply meatfeasts for them.

The bridges away from Tampa call for *Uzita* and *Mocozo*, whisper for *Calusa*. Red painted natives who were swept away three hundred years ago by orange-offering conquistadors and double standard English. Or the braves who remained to be wiped up by the European gift of Yellow Jack, before the U.S. government could force them to Mississippi. All loved the land, but their love was so different. One loved what it was, and one loved what it could become.

Through Orlando the bridges have to holler over the noise of construction and rollercoaster and holidays screaming in a hundred far-reaching languages. The road squeaks out in Timucuan amid fibreglass volcanoes and tubular steel tracks. The street names emblazon their heritage over the traffic, yesterday in lights next to flashing reds.

The I4 continues past the deadzone of Sanford where it moans in Swedish *hör mig via dina mobiltelefoner* and then cries *Ocali* and *Acuera* over the bridges until *Timucua!* in Daytona Beach. Here they were tall, with ash tattoos won through deeds, not display. Ink tattoos remain at the beach, the malls, henna over the feet. A new world is singing, once theirs, now ours and if you listen the road will proclaim it all.

The Quietest Art
Barclay Rafferty

The portable tele, forever troublesome, pops static between jigs and reels. And Dónal's voice, infectious like the song of an otter's den, still goes to and fro with the customer in the back-to-front pullover.

That Size 12 tag really brings out your eyes, etc.

I finger melodies collected mid-nineteenth century, adding a flourish or three for the amusement of Dónal, who interprets notes with appendages, tumbler swishing between wrists, whiskey licking smoothly over ice.

His initiation into silent comedy came when he bunged a birthday gift in the Liffey, only to chirp up moments later in imitation of the making of a ploughman's lunch. When his Ma and Da thought their only son was throwing a fit, Dónal conceded to needing formal training in mime. I asked him one afternoon, bed-ridden and inconsolable, why he tossed the toy in the drink.

Thought Da would fish it out, I suppose.

Physics made him rocket a gangly arm up at school. And when Mr Glackin boat-shoed into the classroom one morning, slurring an apology about being out past midnight at Rathmines Inn watching the group, the seed was planted for young Dónal to swan off to London at eighteen to experience trembling knees and *No, sorrys* firsthand. When offered more rest cures than roles, he sailed home to Dublin, shite-scared of flying.

But in dim lighting, he's still bright, still lithe. Each slow-handed pan from brow to jaw reveals a new masque. To Bertie, he's the gallant lion-tamer; to Cathy, he's the Renaissance painter; to me, he's Dónal, the mate in whiteface and ballet pumps.

—Hurling in the dark; disturbing Father Lunny in the pissing rain to get our ball back; swinging cricket bats like golf clubs, though neither of us owned a pair of white trousers between us.

The bag deflates like an old leather-stripped ball, faraway strains from the pipes inspiring the tongue-tied barman to trace an imaginary tear from his right eye into the puddle in the palm of his left hand. Then he drops the glob in the tumbler with a wink and a tight-lipped grin, and off goes old Back-to-Front Jenny with a cackle and a snifter.

Flight

Anthea Morrison

Again, I said. Dad threw me higher, and I flapped my arms and flew a little way before he caught me, his face gone pale. Two summers later I tried from the apple tree but fell before I could lift my arms and snapped my ankle.

Dad died on his way home from work.

I spent that August in the apple tree, looking at the sky. More summers later I fell in love in a faraway city, and then again, soaring and dipping and singing. I made a mistake and left in the night, my car gliding its way home to a mother I didn't know I still needed.

When I told you, a few dates in, about flying as a little girl, you nodded as though you knew. It was enough. My dress was made of tiny white strips like feathers – like a swan, you said at the reception. That winter, what would have been a baby lay unfinished on my palm like a bird from a smashed egg.

Eventually I watched our child swing high in the playground, launch from the peak of her arc and sail with her arms out wide again and again. I brought home tales from my job at the airport, but you laughed in the wrong places. I didn't ask where you'd gone.

Orphaned, I went home to look for the meadow, for my apple tree. In their place, five new detached houses formed a crescent.

Last summer, our child flown, we found a new freedom heading south through sun-baked fields. We took ourselves by surprise, overcome by a forgotten lust. Back home, you've disappeared again.

Out walking in the rain, those few golden nights shimmer and fade into the mist as I watch two swans make a heart on the lake. I run down the wooden jetty towards them and launch clumsily, arms flapping, and slowly, slowly I gain height.

Intersection, Transit and Rose
Gail Anderson

Marco watched from an unlit window, two storeys up. The old building ticked and sighed around him. Squat housing, an abandoned warehouse backed against indigo strings of railway track. In her flat next door, the nearly famous actor was sleeping. On Transit Street below, a shadow oozed towards her car's passenger window, ghost. Marco stepped across the room, pulled the Sunpac – his largest flash – out of the camera bag.

Obscurity or fame. Everyone here craved one or the other. Parolees, artists, whores. The pretty rentboy on the top floor, a different name each week. The strip-dive, charcoal-sketching drunk who thought he was Toulouse Lautrec. He himself, Marco, flown from a factory job.

His neighbour would soon move on. She'd played the lead in an art film, shot in the desert. Marco, sitting in the dark cinema, felt himself lifted on her luminescence.

Thump. Down in the street, her car roof slapped. Marco thumbed the Sunpac to full power.

He'd seen this done in an old film once, Hitchcock. He pushed the flash out the window, aimed. Covered his eyes with his free hand.

Pop! Red leaves on his shielded eyelids, silent lightning carved crevice and grate, freeze-framed rat and bottle cap. He uncovered his eyes. The shadow was upright now, uncertain. Electronic whine, the flash recycling to power. *Pop!* Hissed profanity from the street below.

Marco watched the shadow seep away. Beyond their common wall, his neighbour slumbered, her shell of dreams unbroken.

So Far Over the Rainbow the Rainbow Is a Fucking Dot

Gaynor Jones

You like your meat red – not pink – red. There has to be blood, there have to be juices flowing, and you have to be able to chew it in that way that *you* think shows your manly jawline, but *I* think makes you look like a sad old man who has forgotten his dentures. I look at your pink gums, and I look at your blue eyes, and I look at the green waitress. I look at the orange curled writing on her name badge, and I sound out the letters with my red tongue on the back of my yellowing teeth. I look at her deep indigo bra strap teasing out from under her grey and red striped uniform. I look at your sweat-pink hand on the creased beige napkin dotted with drooping violets that mops up the red slobber from your mouth, and I wonder if you wipe your mouth that way after you have been between her legs and I feel green bile in my pink throat, not at the thought of you and her. Just at the thought of you. And I think of the rainbow, the one we would have painted, the one we got all the tester pots for but we never got round to painting, and I think how grateful I am now that those two blue lines never appeared and that every month the toilet bowl was red.

The Complexities of Hens
Sandra Arnold

He always set the clock thirty minutes fast so he could enjoy the luxury of having more time than the clock showed. He mended every broken thing in the house with black tape. He welded iron bars onto saucepans whose handles had come off and reminded his four daughters to fill the pans to the brim before they put them on the stove to stop them overbalancing. He trimmed their hair with the kitchen scissors. This wasn't easy as he had the sort of fingers that struggled to pick up small change that had fallen on the floor. He ran up four sets of identical dresses on the sewing machine after he'd finished his cleaning shift at the hospital, using material he'd bought on special. Sewing a straight seam was hard for those fingers, but he wasn't one to shirk his duty. He taught himself how to knit and told the girls not to fret about the dropped stitches in their hats and scarves. He said when he'd mastered the technique, he'd teach them to knit for themselves. He polished their shoes every night until they gleamed, the way he'd learned in the army. He bought six hens and a rooster so there would always be fresh eggs and meat. When the eggs hatched, the girls carried baby chicks in their pockets to keep them warm and gave them names and sang to them as they weeded the vegetable patch and vacuumed the house and did their homework. When all four girls turned up at school one day with black eyes and split lips, they said they'd walked into a door. The youngest said it had nothing to do with refusing to eat the chicken he'd killed and roasted for dinner. She said it had nothing to do with her saying that chickens had feelings and that they had thirty different vocalisations to communicate those feelings. She said it had nothing to do with her sisters saying the chicken he'd roasted was the first one they'd seen climb out of his egg and that they'd watched him grow his new feathers and that he'd just learned to crow.

The Good Samaritan

Rachel Moorhead

He and Isaac had been playing a game – jump into the carriage and out again before the train doors shut. The woman distracted him.

'You get bullied, don't you?'

Pip-tones pinged. Doors closed. Papa's hand on the glass. Mother's cry. Isaac chasing along the platform. He was alone. They were behind.

Tears cut his throat.

The woman smiled a crinkly smile. Her eyes were dark as bedtime.

'We have the same clips.'

Her black gaze followed as he stumbled to the opposite seat. She repeated.

'We have the same clips.'

On her lap sat a strange bag, shiny, with a faded picture of a cat.

She and her bag crossed the aisle to sit next to him. Her breath stank of cheese and onion crisps.

'Hair clips. See.'

Sausage fingers released two clasps. Unruly rain-coloured hair erupted like silver fireworks from behind her ears.

'The same as yours.'

He was clinched, cheek to breast in a single hug. Her body odour stained his sinuses. The cap on the back of his head – inspected. Her voice a whisper.

'It is like a target.'

Two metallic clicks. Cool tickled his crown. Grandfather's bar mitzvah gift in her sweaty hands. The circular woven cloth bought to her nose. Inhaled. His Kippah disappeared into the depths of the cat bag.

A stained pink pencil case appeared. From it, a pair of tiny gold embroidery scissors.

'You won't get bullied again.'

His chin pincered in her left hand. The little scissors in her right. Stubbled grey hairs sprinkled her top lip as her face loomed towards him. He shut his eyes so tight.

The metal was cool against his cheek.

'Snip.'

His chin was turned to the right.

Cool metal again.

'Snip.'

Her smells were gone.

He opened his eyes.

She was down the carriage. Her cat bag in the crook of her arm swinging to the rhythm of the train. A smile soft on her mouth. His curls tight in her fist.

Tending the Garden
Katie Oliver

Nella is often performatively cruel to her husband, even when – no, *especially* when – he wheels out their wedding DVD to entertain guests, for the fucking umpteenth time.

'Give it a rest Gary, no-one gives a shit,' she mutters from the armchair in the corner, red wine and a cigarette on the go. Meanwhile, Gary tries to pretend he isn't embarrassed. He really does try: for Valentine's Day he'd attempted heart-shaped cupcakes, with pink icing and sugar flowers. Cloying. Nella put them on the compost heap, to teach him a lesson. He is still paying off her engagement ring on his credit card.

She would like to leave, of course she would. Except that actually, she can't. Only Gary knows what's buried out there, festering beneath the soil. She walks a fine line between letting off steam and putting herself in danger, stamping on the carpet of eggshells in a temper and then scrambling to stick the shards back together.

'It'll be alright, Nella,' he says, stroking her face in a way that makes her want to commit another murder. He squeezes her arm so hard the purple ghost of his fingertips lingers for days after. 'I love you,' he whispers.

They plant flowers. So many flowers, a manic trip to the garden centre resulting in a bewildering riot of colour. Buds yawn open, lascivious mouths with tongues snaking out. The red lilies had been a mistake.

They let the garden grow out of control. Wildflowers burst through tangled clouds of weeds that suffocate the neglected shop-bought blooms: poppies, crimson and fleeting, oversized daisies, bluebells. They give Nella a migraine.

It is July, and the air wavers in a haze of heat. Wearing only her underwear, Nella takes the secateurs and hacks down anything that grows with barely controlled violence. It takes a long time to destroy everything. Sweat pours down her face and mixes with tears that disappear into the earth so quickly it's as if they were never there.

Gaea Island

E E King

No man is an island, but some women are. Their breasts rise from the deep, their nether regions are covered in brush, and their sandy thighs sink languidly into the sea. These are large women. Lonely women. Women who live with their heads among the fishes and their feet nestled in the deep burning core of the earth.

Leah was one, born from a meeting of a sun and a star. Birds nested in her tree-filled fertile valley. Fresh water flowed from her tear ducts, and though she seldom cried, it was enough to fill a small pond, crowded with fish.

One day a man so emaciated, each bone showed through his skin like rocks beneath rolling hills, was tossed onto her shore.

She quivered. The man feared he had landed on a volcano, but it was only Leah, happy at his touch. He ate her fruit, caught her fish, drank her tears and grew stronger.

At night, he dreamed of the love of a woman as large as the earth.

The man moved down into the fertile basin between Leah's thighs, but soon her valley had borne everything it could. And so, he moved toward the sea, burning trees and brush as he went. He diverted her tears to water his cuttings, and so the pond dried up, the fish died, and the birds flew away. Without birds to spread their seeds, the few trees that had survived the man's forestry, died.

Just as the man was about to expire from thirst and sun, a cruise ship, expanding its route, motored by. The man left, without a backward glance.

In time, Leah grew back her trees and bushes. But she was never the same, she had known love and betrayal, and the scars were visible. Still, when birds came back and nested in new branches, her eyes overflowed, and with no one to divert them, they filled the pond. During a torrential rain, three fish fell from the clouds into her pond. The next year they were ten. Leah flowered. Everything was in harmony.

Until one day, a man was shipwrecked on her shores.

Last Year's Regrets
Michael Loveday

New Year, and already something to be destroyed: a feeling that she wants to leave behind. Scrawl a statement on paper, they tell her. Admit that millionth moment when she acted/didn't act, a guilt that pierced her then and has haunted ever since. Each word she writes reopens that journal she once hid under her childhood bed, confessions that were thrillingly safe, made to no one at all.

Without sharing, they each fold their statements tight and place them inside a bowl. The friends around her now seem suddenly sobered. A tremor runs beneath things she'd thought were their joys – careers, marriages, houses, kids.

On the balcony, framed by a flashing sky, one of the party crouches, leans in with a lighter, sparking it till the papers catch. A flare of orange flame dies down to flickering embers. The scraps that remain are chucked over the rail, spiralling towards the communal garden below. They drift out of sight on gusts of winter air.

Five past midnight: the last of the glitter still hangs in the sky, a barrage of greens, golds, purples. It whispers to her: *change, change.* The dazzle wanes slowly, like the glare of the sun. A memory reluctant to disappear. A body's shame refusing to fade.

Picnic on the Eyot

Julie Evans

There was so much in that one warm sliver of evening that Mother would have disapproved of. The others were strangers really. Stranger danger.

I'd studied the nape of his neck from the row behind in the lecture. His throwaway comment as he turned to pack up. 'We're going on the river tonight, for a picnic. Come!'

The punts were moored up for the night in neat rows like boarding school beds. We broke one free. My first felony. Ed took the pole, and I hunkered down in the low seat with the girls, emasculated. Emma lit a candle in a glass jar, and I watched it shiver a reflection of gold on the water as we moved. Ed knew how to punt, pushing the pole hard into the riverbed, then letting the current slide the length of it between his hands while the dusk bats swooped and flittered around his head. He looked professional, like a gondolier, perfectly balanced on the flat of the stern.

We stopped at an island – an eyot, Ed called it. An island in the river, long and narrow, left to its own devices, the garlicky scent of some wildflower in the air. Picnics at home were miserable affairs, Tupperware boxes and flasks of tea. Folding chairs. Drizzle. Now, we were tearing chunks from baguettes and scooping up dripping Camembert, eating unwashed grapes from a paper bag and downing cheap red wine straight from the bottle. The listeria tasted delicious.

After a while, I walked away to take a pee. Ed joined me. When I zipped up and went to walk back, he held my arm. He leant in for a kiss, and momentarily I returned it, felt myself melting into the softness of his mouth. Chemicals rushed around my body.

I pulled free.

'No, I'm not... you know,' I stammered.

He looked surprised, frowned. 'Sorry, my mistake...' He shrugged, nonchalant. 'Hey-ho.'

I walked away, my head spinning. When I looked back, he was pissing a glorious moonlit arc, a silver rainbow, into the river.

Something swirled under my ribs, as though a vein was unstopped and my blood suddenly flowed free.

The Yo-Yo

Toni Trapani

Consider the yo-yo. A toy of such deliberate whimsy.

Like watching a toddler learning to walk, arms outstretched to the sky, a roly-poly little demigod. A tilt to the right, a tilt to the left, a sudden burst and a diapered butt hitting the ground. Laughter all around! Oh no! The baby is crying. Rock-a-bye that baby.

Can you do Rock-a-bye Baby?

Mr Next-Door-Neighbor taught me that trick in our yard on a bright summers day covered in glittering pink and purple birthday confetti. My neon fairy godfather.

He drew the strings of the yo-yo into a triangle, the small wooden toy moving back and forth between, like the pendulum of a clock. Tick-tock!

And don't forget 'around the world' and 'walk the dog.' So many possibilities in one little toy!

A yo-yo is a sphere, after all. And a sphere is a wheel, and a wheel is the greatest invention of all time. So great that historians mark its creation as the birth of the modern world.

I try to imagine what it would be like to live in the world on the brink of such movement, like a baby when its eyes learn to see the sharp angles of things instead of blurred outlines.

Do you think the men on the line felt this way? One by one up against the wall of their all-day movement. Up and down, to and fro, building the world its freedom.

Mr Next-Door-Neighbor called it the chain gang of life, sitting on the porch with the ice bag on his shoulder. Like the mural by Diego Rivera, he said, painting those bodies caught in motion toward the future while the bodies of five dead lay in the street as reward for their labors.

And I think about that yo-yo in constant motion but going nowhere, sitting in this kitchen with the old lino coming up from the floor.

And my yo-yo lost somewhere in Mr Next-Door-Neighbor's yard a long time ago, amidst the tall weeds I now see reaching up from the ground, like octopus arms encircling the wooden stakes and blotting out the first letter so all that remains is: oreclosed.

Necropolis
Michele Seagrove

What the hell, she thought.

She limped down the track, stopping frequently to adjust her boots. Her feet ached incessantly.

She met no one.

Suddenly she stopped. She was in a glade; a makeshift grave-yard. The centrepiece was a bus, its rusting shell listing gently to one side, tyres and lumps of metal strewn around in the long grass. It was not alone. It was joined by an army of jilted, corroded steeds. Weeds proliferated in their confines, limbs rotting into the earth and innards exposed to the elements. She frowned, contemplating the juxtaposition of the jettisoned jalopies.

The door of the bus succumbed readily, and she stepped aboard, dumping her holdall. She flexed her fingers and sat down with a sigh. The seat covers spilled their guts, and she used some of it to stuff into a yawning gap above her head. Gloves were pulled off. Her hands were bony; skeletal skin red raw. She was too thin all over now, like the pictures of starving children she had seen the last time she watched television. She shivered, and her stomach complained. There was nothing in her holdall today. She would have to go without.

The sun had dipped behind the trees. Night came all too soon this time of year. A blanket was pulled out of her holdall, tattered and dirty, but it was warm, and she wrapped it around her.

'Nice spot of whisky would touch the spot,' she said aloud and laughed, a scratchy sound.

Frost was already forming on the windows of the bus and the grass outside. She would have exclaimed over it in her previous life. Now there were more important things to consider. She hadn't gravitated towards the city, like others had, preferring her old haunts. She tried to lie down across the cramped seats and imagined lying on a soft, warm bed. Her body throbbed, but sleep always came easily enough. She wondered how long it would be before she was moved on.

In the night, the temperature dropped. Finally she was a queen in her mausoleum.

Etched into Vinyl

Kathy Hoyle

There's a tiny scratch in the vinyl. She waits for the needle to jolt with each revolution. It causes a brief inflection in his voice, like a catch in the throat, as though he's taking a breath before each phrase. She pictures him inhaling before he sings out each imaginary piece of her...

Eyes, *ocean blue.*

Lips, *crimson promises.*

Hair, *spun gold.*

Skin, *a silken robe.*

There were other parts to her, of course. Real parts, not-good-enough to make the cut.

Thighs, pulled taut.

Areola, bruised blue.

Mouth, wide and aching.

Teeth, clenched and blood-stained.

He would sit in her window seat, lounging against her floral cushion with tortured arrogance. His long fingers strummed out clichés, lazy green eyes goading her, *this one's for you, baby.* With a tooth-marked pencil, he'd scribble notes onto a bone-white page, stir up chords and choruses that whispered out heady melodies, like incense. Spell-songs. Strawberry summer days, warm beer, sticky-sweet bedsheets, stale cigarette breath. Burns.

She has seen him over the years, on TV, on billboards, even at a festival once. The headline act, singing out his lies, his eyes alive with chemical brightness, his body thinned with fame. She left halfway through. Spent the night with her lover in a clean unclichéd bed.

She pulls down the blinds and opens a bottle of chilled Chablis.

She pities the girl in the song, with her open, willing heart.

The music ends, she lifts the needle and removes the record. Dust has settled on the cover, like ash. She pushes the record back into its sleeve and carefully slides it in amongst the many others. She turns off the lamp, sinks into the sofa and sips the Chablis. It softens the sting.

The memory fades into the shadows, but the song remains.
A scar, etched into vinyl.

The Glove

John Stephens

It's not the safest place to cross. Cars are parked on both sides. It's dangerous because they jump the lights. There is a crossing, but it's just too far along.

She dropped the glove as she started to cross. I picked it up – mohair, soft, like a black kitten.

I called after her. I was going to give it back. She was tall and slim and had one of those black woollen berets – same as the gloves, and a scarf to match. She looked very French. I wanted her to be French because in our story we are in Paris.

She was halfway out when she turned her head. As she turned, her hair spilled across her shoulders, glistening red in the sunlight.

She hadn't seen the lights change. She smiled, I think. I'll never know for sure.

In my room the light is cold. The bed is the only warm place. I snuggle down under the duvet, take out the glove and slip it on. And it's like we're holding hands. I feel it soft against my cheek, her perfume on my lips, like the scent of jasmine.

In my story she smiles.

Alice Forgets Everything but the Watermelons
Olivia Kingery

When she gets to the grocery store, Alice smells the fresh melon being cut. It is June, and summer is a shade of lip color everyone is wearing. The floors are waxed, and her tennis shoes glide over the linoleum. The squeak is a pitch above the radio. People stare. She is wet from swimming in the lake, and maybe she forgot to wring out her hair, or maybe she never put her cover-up back on, maybe. She forgets her list in the car, digs aimlessly in her purse, and decides she will have to guess.

- Watermelon
- Limes
- Fingerling potatoes
- Charcoal

There was something before the charcoal, but it is gone now. Maybe a meat, or a beverage, lemonade most likely, gin even likelier, but there is nothing, so she moves on. The man cutting the watermelon is smiling. He throws the knife down hard, over and over, as if the rind were a shell and the flesh was, well, flesh. She winces. He is offering samples of honeydew, cantaloupe, and watermelon. Her shoes squeak closer. Instead of using the rind as a convenient container, he ends each thwack of butcher's knife into a plastic cup. Quaint, she thinks. He smiles at customers without looking at the melon or the knife or his hands so close to the edge. Alice thinks he is smiling just at her. Alice can't tell if she is smiling back. She wants melon, but the knife, and the grinning, and the squeaking is too much.

When Alice gets home, she can't remember leaving the store. Panic memory loss is what google told her one time she found herself at the grocery store's parking lot, reversed situation of now. Sitting in the car with the radio off, she sighs, runs her hands through her hair, and looks at the dozens of watermelons in her backseat. Too much, she thinks.

Indulgence

Lee Nash

Alone with the Father, yet not completely, I'm glad of the distraction, the unconditional love, unconcerned as a steamy nose bores the dark fabric covering my groin. A perfect carnal beast, he changes course, makes to gnaw the Bible that lies invitingly open, its leather back arched against the polished glass.

Father's in jeans, wears a simple gold cross. He has doe eyes, and a prominent lump swells where his third one is thought to be. I have much to say but hesitate. The words catch like burrs in my throat.

I want to tell him a part of me is missing. Like the bread he holds up to heaven, a sector withdrawn from the circle. That I'm out of place – an insuppressible yawn in the mass, a sneeze in the gush of the Lord's prayer.

We don't discuss the past. Instead, he makes me feel welcome, absorbs my awkwardness, reads me like a living psalm. He's accustomed to the broken, the faint, the weary. I fold up lines carefully prepared.

Before I leave, he walks towards an armoire, reaches in for something. Surely not a bottle of wine... perhaps a catechism, a devotional planner. He offers me a smooth plastic cylinder – a much more appropriate gift. I rally from my double-take, obligingly roll the barrel over my thighs, collecting the coarse white hairs that cling to my black woollen tights.

'Otherwise,' he adds, half-embarrassed half in jest, 'when you walk down the street, people will know you've been with the Father.'

I smile, hand him the gathered moult of his dog.

Father, that's exactly what I want.

Nevermore

D Larissa Peters

She lays under him, body flattened. She thinks, even in this moment she can wax poetic: now is my heart flattened too? The weight of his body seems to seep into her. A comforting feeling as she recalled the moments.

Thirty-five. Virgin. Waiting. Not waiting. Telling. Asking. Tired. But not tired of waiting. Just tired of the worry from her parents. Tired of the endless questions of 'But why?' one way or another.

He starts moving, rolls over next to her. Says probably the most cliché thing she's ever heard, 'Was it as good for you as it was for me?'

She nearly burst out laughing but instead gives a little sigh that she hopes sounds encouraging. She rolls out of bed, holding her breasts and tiptoes to the bathroom. She allows herself a smile, a little laugh even while she dresses and walks out the door.

Now she feels cliché. Now she is just part of the Plenty of Fish that swims directionless, wandering, bouncing like amoebas under a microscope so unaware that they are not only being watched, but they are swimming in a very contained space.

Her T-shirt isn't warm enough for September, but she doesn't really mind as she allows herself to think back to a warm evening in June. Her father hooks a necklace around her ten-year-old neck. She's sober in a moment of glorified promise, 'I will remain pure until my wedding day.' She is aware of her father blowing his nose and her mother looking serious and pleased. And the feeling inside her of, 'I'm growing up.'

And somewhere along the way, that belief held fast within her. Hooked in her heart like Edgar Allen Poe's Raven with Biblically proportionate claws: 'Nevermore.'

This analogy pleases her, even as she slowly got into her car. She felt in pain, as she knew she would, but it felt a minor stretching, and she didn't mind too much. 'Quoth the Raven, "Nevermore."'

She sits down and shifting into first, remembers that no amount of ignoring the Raven's claws could take away the blood now leaking from the wounds beneath her.

Empty Shoes

Joanna Cohen

Always check in your shoe, he said. Dad had grown up in Egypt, Saudi, Iraq. Scorpions lived in the toe wells and needed to be knocked out. So, I did. In Croydon, my black patent Mary Janes; in Bexleyheath, my Converse sneakers and in Elstree, a pair of lace-ups, suitable for all weathers.

'Come on,' mum would scold every morning, grabbing at bags, hats, lunches, wallets and keys. She would jam her feet into boots, or stuff her toes into slip-ons, walking fast into her shoes, already on her way out the door. I learned to make my peeks furtive, worked on sliding my fingers into the leather depths so she wouldn't notice, the empty indentations of my toes a smooth reassurance.

She always saw. From the front step, her feet poised on our shabby mat caked in old mud, her shoulders and neck twisting against the delay.

'Why bother?' she'd ask, once the door was safely shut and locked behind us. Our hurried tread scuffed the broken pavement slabs and slippery leaves. Because I needed to know, I would think, as I skirted the cracks and hopped the curb. Because to forget was to risk the sting; to lose the chance of remembering how he had always kept me safe.

'What's the point?' she'd mutter as we parted at the school gate. Her lips, cracked in the cold, would skim my hair, catching strands of my carefully brushed ponytail on the edges of her skin. And I would curl my toes into a secret clump, squeezing the rough fabric of my socks, scrunching them painfully into the damp interior of my shoes. Then, my fingertips would slip from her dry grasp, as she pushed back and away, elbowing through the eddies of parents, into the current of her day.

The Heart of Every Faint Smell Remembered
Anne Howkins

Stop buying lilies for the sitting room; none of them has any smell. Pick bland leaves from the rampant mint, wonder if it needs watering. Complain that a new bottle of Coco Chanel has gone off. Ask your teenage son if he's discovered deodorant.

The consultant offers sympathy. There are no answers, maybe this drug, maybe that. Perhaps a scan will show us... perhaps not.

At home, stalk through the house. Stand in each room, eyes closed, touching nothing, muting every sense but smell. Your olfactory neurons refuse to connect with anything. Weep quietly.

You long to breath honeymoon lavender fields, Provence heat sweating out piney floral notes, scenting the mistral swirling round his old MG, fighting its reek of hot oil and hidden just-married kippers.

Hanker for the scent of lilies, leitmotif of your marriage. Glorious raspberry ripple stargazer trumpets, that heavy, heady bouquet so overpowering you would open the French windows, set the scent molecules loose. Catch up with them later in the velvet night, lying on your backs in the overgrown cemetery next door, finding Cancer and Sagittarius while summer grass tickled your noses and naked bodies.

Yearn to sniff out your babies, milky sweet as you rubbed your face over giggling tummies, pudgy fingers pulling your hair. Echoes of Johnson's Baby Shampoo on damp heads, dark curls winding themselves as tight as your love. The fragrance of belonging, a tiny finger wrapped around yours.

Empty the laundry basket on the bathroom floor. Snuffle your way through sweaty arm-pitted office shirts, musky teenage crop tops, reeking football socks, damp soapy towels, unmentionable knickers – a bloodhound's delight, your disappointing olfactory desert.

Find old party balloons in a kitchen drawer. Carry them everywhere.

Inflate your balloons with the bouquet of fresh coffee; cat-piss elderflower; nutmegged rice pudding; post-thunder petrichor; hay ready for baling; candy floss, greasy hot dogs and crackling dodgems; nan's violet posies; cast-off ballet shoes; your absent husband's crumpled pillow... add to your treasury of odours every day.

Store the balloons under your bed until the doming mattress rolls you to the floor. Sleep caressing the rubber, letting each aroma diffuse into your dreams.

The Disconcerting Discovery of Shoes on a Beach
Elaine Mead

The first time he walked out, he disappeared for two days. So we waited.

One of his moods, we thought. *He'll be back.*

And he was.

We walked along the beach and told him. We said he shouldn't do these things. It made us worry. Hands in pockets, eyes out to sea, he didn't say where he'd been.

He said he wouldn't do it again. But he did.

The fourth time, we didn't see him for eight days. He came back with a bruise on his cheek, shoes missing and sand between his toes. Dishevelled hair with seafoam secrets. He ate all the eggs and what was left of the bread. Dripped bright yellow yolks and sweet apologies. We clutched our hands to our breast bones in mock heartbreak.

Don't do it again, we begged.

I won't, he lied.

It became a dance we didn't want to follow, though it suited him to lead. He liked the part but forgot his shoes. Said he lost them. We bought him new ones.

The next time he came back with shells for eyes and starfish hands. We didn't want to see.

Look, he said.

Come back, we pleaded.

I will, he said.

On the countless time after countless days, we walked along the beach. Remembered that first time. *He'll be back,* we thought.

The dog found them. The shoes we bought him. Half buried, laces tangled with seaweed. Tongues lolling, wet and lapping at the sand.

He'll be back.

Amicable

Andrea Anderson

He says he talks about you in therapy like he's giving you a gift.

A compliment.

An excuse.

You think of countering with a story about your herb garden, the one you're trying to grow on your partially covered balcony – fragile clay pots of mint and cilantro and thyme and oregano and spruce thistle stalks of fragrant, gray-green rosemary, little Sharpie-scratched vinyl spears sticking out of the dirt to remind you which is which, like wiggling, bleach-bright, horror-film skeleton fingers protruding from the fog in a graveyard.

You find a pair of his socks under the couch, balled up with the dust motes and the popcorn kernels; you wash them before you throw them out. You even use fabric softener.

There are recipes bookmarked on your phone, oregano-crusted chicken thighs and garlic-rosemary focaccia. You put them all into one folder and label it something misleading, something less embarrassing – because you aren't going to make those recipes, because you're never going to make any of those recipes, because he's the scream you learned to swallow and the fist you learned to bite and the sour greasy burnt-brittle wave of bile and nausea and resentment you learned to *listen* to, that's still sloshing around your empty, concave stomach, and there isn't room left over for anything else.

He writes you a letter.

An apology.

An excuse.

He doesn't mail it. He reads it to you on your doorstep, the cuffs of his expensive, crisply ironed shirt rolled up to his elbows. It's pale, gutless, corner-cubicle blue; the shirt, not the letter. His watch is shiny. His eyes are shinier. He waits for a while after he's done, staring at you, studying you, like he's expecting for you to produce a letter – an apology – an excuse of your own. Like you owe him that. Like your destruction was mutually assured, a demon deal gone awry, a shattered mirror with two sides and no frame and a dozen

179

– a hundred – a thousand jagged edges. Papercuts. Bloody hand-prints.

You have earth and lyme and glass and basil leaves trapped beneath your fingernails.

A packet of marjoram seeds in your pocket.

Ghost Child

Donna L Greenwood

The child is too young to catch the bus on her own. You know this. She'll arrive at school seventy minutes too early. The school gates will be locked, and she'll have to wait on the street. You know this, but you watch her walk to the bus stop, and you pray that nothing bad will happen to her. You need her to leave the house by seven so that you can get to work on time. You need this job; it will save you both, one day.

She wakes up crying in the night. He holds you down in bed so you can't go to her. *She's attention seeking*, he says.

She spills her juice on his coffee table. You hold your breath. He shouts at her, and you try not to see her lips squeeze together as she fights back the tears.

He wipes her fingerprints from the mirror in the lounge. You sit very still as he tells her to go to her room. You watch as she nods and flees upstairs.

There is no trace of your daughter in his house. Her presence is stuffed into the back bedroom. She is a ghost child; a wraith haunting the upstairs of the house, oh so very quietly.

At night, you drink wine and laugh too loudly. He tells you your daughter is a cunt. You look up at the ceiling and hope she's sleeping.

When you are not at work, and she's at school, and he is wherever he is, the walls of his house slam down and surround you. On days like these, the fear is incarnate, its grip relentless. You hold her teddy bear to your face and breathe in the smell of her. It smells like new life, and for a moment the fear subsides, and possibilities bloom before you. But then her smell evaporates and all you are left with is the odour of his cigarette smoke which swirls around you even though he left the house hours ago.

Mountain Woman

Pique Allens

A man is a balcony, a tiny surface to stand on and reach for fresh air. A man is not a home. She's been muttering a lot, lately. She trips on a bared root, stumbles, catches her balance and smiles. These crumbly paths are to her liking: sandy stone and brush life, contorted pines, and the occasional dent in the mountainside – not enough of a cavern to keep her safe, but enough to feel that her outlook is immense and the panorama pleasing. The woman has found her natural place. Her feet are coarse and no longer bleed.

She remembers there were times when she had a man. She had a job, too. She made things small and flawless. She'd go home to her small flat in the Eixample, off Diagonal, and if she was lucky, she'd hook up with a guy who was a cushion, or a cloud. Often the chance encounter was just with a fridge boy, nothing warm to the touch, and the cold gnawed at her inside.

This last time, the guy had felt like a cup that she could drink from, and then he turned into earphones that told her what to do. She wrapped his head in a baby blanket and rolled it into the corner of the room. She didn't need to fit much else into her gym bag.

Now she lives in the mountains of Andorra. Her stare will freeze any creature in its steps. She can skin a raccoon in less time than you need to say 'check, mate'. That meat is raw and foul, the chew unsatisfactory. Yet there is warmth. All she wants is a glass of cava from time to time, and for the skull to talk back and agree with her, unquestioning.

Spiders and Flies

Jupiter Jones

The door clicks shut, and I sigh. Not with longing or regret. I lean against the wall, there in my narrow hallway, freckled with mildew; that slight smell of damp. Two of the last leaves from the sycamore tree have come in as he went out. They lie together on the doormat, their summer bloom long gone, now disfigured and spotted black. I go to the bedroom and open the blinds. Outside it is dusk; the street-lights buzz with sodium glare as the night-city lights up, illuminating our nest. I look at the bed, decide to leave it unwashed, unmade. Maybe I will sleep in our sex sheets all week.

I go to the bathroom and pull the light-cord which can be heard in the flat above as a dull click under the floorboards. Put in the bathplug, turn on the taps, the waterpipes clank somewhere below. A spider scurries from the advancing water, and I stoop and scoop, lifting her up to the safety of the dusty plastic foliage on the shelf above. I open my hands, and for a moment she clings to me with the slenderest of legs, a hair's breadth. Her body is pale and speckled. She weighs nothing. Presently, elegantly, she stretches out; one leg, another, and another, reaching for the new place where she will spin her gossamer lies.

I regard my body in the mirror. I imagine him standing behind me. His body, hairy with a fine dark down. Mine waxed bald. He has the advantage of size, muscularity, a fullness; but I have cunning, patience. I gaze at my pubis, domed like a skull cap, pebble, eggshell. Run a finger along thin collarbones, down my skinny arms, jointed, articulated; sniff my fingers. I turn off the taps, not ready yet to be washed of him, his attentive kind.

I dress and walk to the bar on the corner. More easy flies.

Bright Memories

Sharon Boyle

Layla has been barred from three of the town's five pubs through an antisocial trinity of brawling, bawling and cursing. One pub has pinned her polaroid behind the bar – mouth mid-swear, eyes feral. Nobody has seen her sober; only charged-up and alight. That, or pitched over the kerb, silent and staring.

Last week she arrived in pub four, smoked a cigarette in blatant view of the barman and was ejected pronto.

A man at the bar pushed back his glass and stood, saying, I knew her from before. When she was light on her feet, bright in her eyes and spoke without slurring.

Something must have happened, the other patrons claimed, wanting to know more, but the man shrugged on his jacket and left.

The mystery was rolled around, elaborated and stretched before fading into yesterday's news.

*

Tonight Layla enters pub five. Claims she is hot, suffocating; strips off her dress to display scarred, saggy skin. A finger points to the door, and she lurches outside, followed by the pub congregation – a mobile theatre audience eager for entertainment. She skitters on the cobbles and turns to the crowd, hands splayed in appeasement, shouting, *I meant no harm. No harm at all.*

She shivers in her underwear and glances down at her tights, ripped. A shame, for it took all her concentration getting them on.

Her dress lands at her feet. Slung by the man who knew her from before, when she was light and bright; when she smoked freely; when she hadn't concentrated enough; when she'd meant no harm; when the house went on fire, and she ran upstairs and was blocked by thick, choking smoke; when she had two children; when it made the papers. A tragedy that faded in everyone's mind, except hers. For Layla it is always today's news.

This Iguana Feeds Almost Exclusively on Algae

Rachel Maloney

She had to balance on a chair to thump its back, but with a final bit of coaxing the radio static-ed into life. It clung to the top of the fridge with the power cord coiled tightly around its chest as she sat down at the kitchen table.

'So, yes, of course we should add something about domestic violence to the national curriculum,' the presenter said. He sounded bedraggled. She imagined his studio was in some form of marshland, and he was at gunpoint.

What he was saying made sense, she reasoned. *Young boys these days, well – unless their father taught them properly, they weren't leaving school with the right skills for it. Somewhere down the line, that'd result in a workplace shortage, and eventually women would have to pick up the slack.*

As she submerged her nose into her mug and listened to the man prattle on about workplace violence, she felt her £700 a month universe ripple around her. Not much. Like something had just slipped into the water from the surface and dived down into the dark. *Would the police come?* she wondered. She hadn't heard anyone call them.

Her coffee had iridescent scales on top from the limescale in the kettle, like an iguana had crawled in to wash off the remains of a rough shed. She hoped faintly that it wouldn't cut its feet on the chipped handle or slip on the broken pieces of smashed crockery on the floor.

If it had been a screenplay, she would have taken a slow and meaningful look at what used to be someone's favourite bowl, then silently, artistically, started to laugh and/or cry.

Instead, she took another sip of scaly coffee and waited.

The Mailman

Amy Barnes

I drove over the cardboard roadkill. Flattened into another road layer; the tape and recyclable lunch bag paper vermin needed to die. Blacked-out return addresses of forgotten and unforgiven senders. Guilty gift remnants clinging to packing peanuts, box folds, marked-fragile manilla envelopes. Tire tracks tattooed black memories across each one.

It was against mailman code to damage mail. I always drove carefully like my mail truck cushioned unborn baby bird junk mail, baby chicks shipped to farms, bills, catalogs, brown-wrapped nudie magazines and rose-scented grandma cards with ten-dollar birthday checks.

'Neither snow, nor rain, nor heat, nor gloom of night stays these courageous couriers from the swift completion of their appointed rounds.'

Even though they were Herodotus' words and didn't belong to the US Postal service, I never missed my route in twenty years. Not one day. Not on my rural route from the wrong side of the car. Not in the snooty McMansion zone.

When I wrote my wedding vows, I wanted to use those words. I will love you in snow, rain, heat and gloom of night. They meant more than traditional words. To me at least. Anna created romantic vows about midnight milkshakes and our adopted turtle. I never thought we would have a swift completion of our married appointed rounds. I never thought my nights would be gloomy.

I yelled echoing vows into my empty mail truck. I screamed the funny punny post office references, my version of romance. The history of love stamps and our love. Our new paired names calligraphed in the return address section. How many days it took for us to fall in love compared with priority mail delivery, just two to three days after I met her. On time. Never late. Not stopped by the blizzard swirling around our first kiss.

I drove over the mail to hold it down. Over all the sympathy cards, unopened ignored bills, donations to her favorite charity. I spotted the familiar LOVE on an envelope and stamped it with mail truck grief before leaving our driveway.

It was still early enough to finish my route.

Spare Room

P J Stephenson

I'll tell you why.

I was in a trance for ten weeks. Numb. Immune to sensations, devoid of emotions.

I felt like I was walking around in someone else's house. The sights, smells, noises. None affected me.

The theme tune of his favourite TV show.

The porch door opening with the swish and clunk that used to herald his return from golf.

The shoes lying in the hallway, polished to military-grade shininess for the club dinner dance.

His aftershave, wafting off of the lawyer's suit.

His car in the drive, parked hurriedly at an angle as he tried to make it inside before the football started.

The sports bag in the bedroom, packed with his overnight things for the minibreak in the Lake District we never took.

When I started to reawaken, I also started to adapt to my new life. And, yes, I keep my towels in the spare room now. I prefer them warm and sweet-smelling from the airing cupboard on the landing. But I put him in there for safe-keeping.

The urn looks too fancy to leave on the mantlepiece. It might tempt burglars.

So that's why, as I pull a cold, dank towel from the drawer, I start to cry.

Stitches

Damien Mckeating

I looked down and noticed the stitches in my skin. They were faint and hard to see; just a pale line in my flesh, with a trail of dots on either side. I found more of them. My body was crisscrossed with them. I was a patchwork man.

The significance of this became apparent when I visited my father. He was old. Time had left him lesser somehow. Once he had stood tall and strong, now he was bent and thin. Where we had once looked eye to eye, I stood a full head taller than him. As I had grown up and gone out into the world, he had fallen in on himself and become lost in his books and his home. It was as if we had passed each other and I imagine there was a point in time where we would have been equal.

I saw the stitches on his skin too.

I traced their paths, these road maps across our skins. I saw the patterns. I saw how he had become weaker as I had grown stronger. I saw how he had given me confidence, while he shrank from the world. I saw how he had taught me to laugh, while he had become bitter in his old age.

He had taken himself apart and given me the things he thought I needed.

I saw then, on his skin, patches of my grandfather: his skill with his hands, his prejudices, his ability to memorise roads and directions.

Look at us; these patchwork men. Were we ever truly whole? Is there any part of us that is just ourselves? I am afraid to look.

I stand in the nursery and look down at my son. He is unblemished, and I am relieved. He, at least, will be himself.

I hope he is wise.

I hope he believes in himself.

I hope he is able to laugh.

And I realise that I can give him those things.

I look down at my skin and my stitches.

I take up the scissors.

And I start to cut.

Within Reach

Hannah Cole

She had a strange sneeze, the sound like a bottle of fizzy drink being popped open. How unromantic, that I remembered the sound of her sneeze over anything else – not her laughter, spilling away from me like all the years of our acquaintance; not her voice, soft and cutting as it wrapped around the word camomile – no, in that café, on that afternoon, I heard her sneeze and I ducked beneath the table, as if there was an earthquake drill.

My world had been shaken, I suppose. She had become a memory to me. I could look at her, that part of my life was still transparent, but when I reached in her direction, I touched glass. I remembered how we used to sit in the middle of the street. It never occurred to us to be afraid of cars. We formed a barricade with our little bodies and ran circles around each other, and she was so much faster than me. I was always reaching for her and touching only the ends of her long hair, taunting me like a kite I had hoisted to the wind but was now failing to bring back to earth.

Once, she stopped to sneeze. I had cats, and she had dogs, and on any given day, she was allergic to one or the other, but never both. Perhaps one had walked past at that moment. Or maybe the pollen was high, although I didn't know what pollen was then, as much as I pretended to her that I did. It could have been the cold air, tickling her nose with the promise of the approaching winter. It could have been luck. But she sneezed, and I put my hand on her shoulder and said: *got you.*

Back in the café, I could have done the same. She was close. But I didn't run after her. I left the café before the second sneeze, and in the street, some children were playing – like ghosts of our younger selves. I started running, too, but not in circles, just away, because I no longer wanted to touch what was within reach.

Relationship Maths

Dettra Rose

Our bed has two countries. A border we don't cross.

His snore has a whistle. I'm clad in flannelette. Before, when our bed was still one country, maths didn't figure much in our relationship.

When we talk about it, left-over feelings scratch my throat. His too. I hear them. Then we put on Netflix.

Voices rise next door. Neighbour's secrets arrive intact through baking-paper walls. Most mornings I see her latching the door. We look at each other for seven heartbeats, then smile. We own the same pale eyes.

It's Saturday night. I put on glamour, he changes his T-shirt, we go to dinner.

I tell him a new position has come up at work, I might apply. And can we please move so we don't have to hear our neighbours burp?

He agrees about the flat, then rants about his idiot boss micromanaging him. We should save for a holiday. Greece? Chilli sauce drips down his chin. I pass a serviette.

Home in bed. I switch off the light.

'Are you awake?'

I cross the border to his side. My heart's a flapping fish.

I'm violently lonely in my country. Isn't he?

I'll give my husband what he really wants. More than a new boss, a better flat, a Greek Island holiday. Me. My skin. My enduring longing. If only he'll stop tallying the moments we reached across and found ourselves outcast. If he'll look at me without that tired spreadsheet hardening his eyes.

I trace a kiss between his shoulder blades.

I'm here in your country. Turn around, please.

Or we can hurt privately. Stay in our pods and carry on keeping score. Crunch numbers so they can shut us down some more.

Roll over and hold me. Love-bomb me, feel my withered skin ripen like plump summer fruit.

How to Fold a Crane

Rachel Fung

Pre-fold paper according to the diagram shown for the creases will help guide you.

Most high-rise office buildings in the city had a certain scent. Not the same scent. But they were almost all always pleasant, always sweet, always light. So light that most of the buildings' occupants barely noticed it. But they brought that scent with them as they went out into the world. The high-rise building people. Marked by that scent; the absence of the smell of human sweat.

Fold both the right and left edges inwards to the centre. Repeat for the other side.

He noticed the jar his first day there. A large glass jar that was about twelve inches high by five inches wide. It sat to the left of the old security guard's small wooden desk, which stood outside by the electronic barriers. The electronic barriers through which suits and heels crisply entered and exited the building, lanyards swinging around collective necks.

Fold the bottom along the dotted line to form a tail.

It started with one or two initially but one lunch break he had lost count of the number of paper cranes. Now they filled nearly a third of the jar. Quiet riot of colour and bodies; pink brushing yellow crushing blue, tail by head embraced by wing. He nearly stopped one day with an urge to ask the old guard whether he was keeping count, but the push of impatient suits on his back at the barriers stopped him, and he dropped it.

Partially fold down wings and open by pulling wings slowly apart.

He had not seen the old guard around for nearly a week now. Nor the glass jar. The new guard ignored the building's occupants with the same studiousness that was dealt him, and everyone was comfortable. Rarely smiled except at his phone. He nearly stopped one day with an urge to ask the new guard where the old guard and his cranes had gone, but the rush of his colleagues before him stopped him and he dropped it.

To complete, blow gently into the body to expand and give it life.

Flotsam

Jo Withers

My father said my mother was a mermaid.

On her birthday we'd always picnic at the beach. I'd take white flowers from the garden, thread them onto string with shells and buttons and leave them in a rock pool just for her. Sometimes I'd find puddles of shiny rocks and pearlescent beads on our doorstep and know that she'd passed by. And the year I learnt to read my father brought home notes and drawings from my mermaid mother, rolled tight in small glass bottles that he said he'd found on fishing trips.

My father said she couldn't live near land for long, the ocean's call was much too powerful. He said when I was tiny, she'd hold me tight on her back and dip in and out of the water like a dolphin while I giggled in her ear. He said her eyes were bright as sardine scales whenever she held me, our yellow curls mingling together on the surface of the sea like tidal foam.

Of course, the other girls at school were jealous. One called me a liar. Said her own non-mermaid mother told her that when I was very young, my mother dropped me at her friend's one day and never came to pick me up.

Sometimes in the bath, I lie back and try to hold my breath beneath the water to test if my lungs work like a mermaid child. I can feel my chest get tighter, and the edges of my vision begin to speckle black like the world is closing in on me. I know I need to get out quickly before the darkness wins. I guess that's how my mermaid mother felt when she tried to live with us on land.

But my father's breath is constant and calm. When I snuggle on his lap, I listen as it spirals around the cavity of his chest and hear a lifetime of love resonate within that hollow space just as every whisper of the ocean can be held within a single shell.

Saline

Douglas W Milliken

The wife is talking so, and I'm laughing. I'm on my side on our ever mistreated couch, my wife is talking, and I'm laughing to beat Jesus. In a too-small T-shirt that might actually be hers – so small almost all my soft belly lies exposed – and brand-new underwear because even fuckups sometimes deserve nice things, and I'm laughing full and loud and without hope of control while my wife tells her story – she's in the three-legged wingback in the corner across from me, legs crossed but arms out like even she can't believe what she's saying – and I have no idea what she's talking about. Black hair like a mythic waterfall. Tight-knit dress like something our hot, young grandmas would've worn. What's she talking about? What's she telling me? The cat lolls on the rug in its 7 A.M. boredom, and my wife tells a story that might be a memory or might be a dream or might maybe just be something she one time heard (who can say?), and I am laughing like lives depend on it, countless tiny lives, or anyway, three lives. These three lives. My wife and my cat: I'm laughing to keep us alive. My inner arm burns still and itches while my bones continue their quaking – that's what it feels like, like steady tremors thrumming my marrow – and I know I won't eat for another day yet, but that's okay. I'm set. The wife's voice. The cat attacking its tail. My laughter. Drawn from a well deeper than whatever. Scraped of everything that isn't pure. I'm set. She raises her arms to look at her hands – first one, then the other, then the first, then the other – as if she's never seen them before. Pillow wet with tears. Being clean's never felt so.

When Plan A Goes Awry

Lisa Ferranti

Dani's hands are dirty. She digs in soil beneath the rose bushes in the condo's community garden, ignoring Blake, who's weeding next to her. She forgot her gloves, and her fingernails collect grime. She tries not to picture her nails raking Blake's back just an hour before. The *audacity*, she thinks, trying to avoid other 'A' words that crowd her mind.

She's still surprised she's attracted to a man the same age as her father, a detail she's concealed from him on their weekly calls. Another concealed detail: Blake is married. The disease Blake's wife has: *Alzheimer's*. It doesn't absolve Dani, but she uses the knowledge to assuage her guilt.

Mrs Crandle, the condo association president, gives her a purse-lipped smile, and Dani nods, looks away. She imagines that everyone sees a scarlet 'A' emblazoned across her chest. She recalls the family-folklore her dad tells: how at age three she ate a little wooden 'A' tile from the Scrabble game. She wonders now if that incident branded her somehow, marked her as a future *Adulteress*.

A prickly weed pokes her finger, and she yanks her hand upward, scraping it against the bush's thorns. A line of red dots appears on her knuckles. Blake removes one glove, pulls a white handkerchief from his pocket, offers it to her, their arms brushing in the exchange. She pulls away as if her skin has been singed.

She remembers her highest scoring Scrabble word ever, during a game with her dad when she was younger: *Vixen*, the X on a triple letter, plus double word. She was so proud of herself, the word holding no meaning then other than *Score!*, a time when her plan didn't include being a mistress, when all 'A' stood for was *Apple*.

Role Model
Paul Karp

I'm telling myself it doesn't matter if the piece is good or not, as he regales the barbecue guests with his perceived triumph. The circle had shrunk – most had caught the whiff of likely failure early and had absented themselves. I felt responsible because I had brought him here, the groom-to-be was sure our shared profession would give us plenty to discuss on the car ride up, a trip which stretched out interminably from the moment he got in.

The piece was about a cancelled octopus tossing competition, the unlikeliest of subject matter intended to be the pudding in the proof of his singular talent. Every line seemed to contain a knowing wink for the careful reader, but I spent the duration isolating individual phrases for any hint that it was not age that separates us but some more fundamental flaw. He used the word 'cephalopod' – so perhaps pride – and then 'culture war' – so perhaps a tendency to cliché. But then I remembered that is a mark against his style and not his character, taking me back to the starting point of pretending I don't need this piece to be terrible, truly terrible, to come away from the encounter unscarred by a premonition of my own failure.

It finished with a meditation on the quality of life of the untossed octopus. There was hesitation in declaring the council had come to the Right Decision because perhaps a life of meaning is better than one without suffering.

'What a remarkable piece!'

'Bet that put them on the map!'

The first reviews veiled the truth with careful euphemisms.

But then came the final word: 'Exquisite.' The groom needn't have spoken at all; a single tear rolling down his cheek was review enough.

Just as I feared: words cannot save us.

Stand Up

Charlie Swailes

She stands up eating in the kitchen. Cream crackers topped with butter, cheese, ham. Crumbs litter her top, falling down her body and creating a light dust on the floor. She always eats this way. Handfuls of rice from plastic, microwaved tubs. Pasta in fingertips, dipped in crimson sauce. Sprinkles of grated cheese dispensed from above directly into her mouth, all whilst standing or walking around, leaving meandering lines of debris in her wake.

The idea of sitting to eat is foreign, goes against her instincts. Putting food on a table seems wrong. Waiting for others to eat too feels strange. Forks and spoons are bizarre artefacts; they would look peculiar in her naïve hands, like a pen in a baby's clumsy fist.

You enter the kitchen. You sigh when you see her, again, leaning against the beige kitchen counter. She is always doing this. This disgusting habit infuriates you. Clicking your tongue, you begin passive-aggressively sweeping, nudging her feet unnecessarily. She takes another bite. You boil over.

'Use cutlery, for God's sake. Why can't you eat at a table? You make the place a mess. What's wrong with you?'

You do not know about the punishments. You do not know about the fear. You cannot think of this woman as a young girl with dirty hair and torn clothes, her skinny frame hiding in corners, squatting in shadows, hoping to remain part of the darkness. You cannot comprehend that food, once found or stolen, needed to be eaten quickly, gobbled up before large, rough hands could smack it away, large, rough boots crushing it into the filthy floor and hot, rough breath could speak terrible words of 'worthless' and 'disgust' and 'punishment'.

Perhaps if you did know, you would stand up with her and smile as you snap a cracker to share, your fingers greasy with butter, your clothes marked with crumbs.

But instead you remain on the floor, tutting at the dust.

Some Consolation

Aileen O'Farrell

My sister's the worst. Falling through the front door, all mascara and snot. Arms dragging around my neck 'til I nearly fall on my arse in the hallway. Her Jack Russell racing around, lashing our ankles together with his lead. I make us a pot of tea.

'Bacardi,' she bleats, and I've to climb up on the stool to get the bottle off the top of the press. Pain ripping through me.

'Cheer up, Noelle,' I say, dunking a ginger nut. 'It could be worse. It could be you.'

And she's off again, wailing. I pat her on the shoulder. You wouldn't believe how many people I've consoled in the past week.

My own kids are diamonds. White-faced with the effort of holding their shit together and keeping my spirits up. I want to tell them there's no need, but that'd just upset them further and anyway it gives them something to do for now.

Some people making the pilgrimage – aunties, neighbours. Others that I'll never see again in this life. There's some comfort in that. To know that Joan from Accounts won't be pestering me for any more mileage forms. That I'll never again have to watch Sweaty Simon from Claims masticating a pork pie across the canteen table.

'We'll make you a bucket list.' She crunches an ice-cube. Takes out a pen.

At this point I'm supposed to be coming out with pearls of wisdom. Facebook homilies. Instagram quotes. Things I wish I'd done more of, things I wish I'd done less of. Swimming in the sea. Making pancakes. Hiking to Machu Picchu. The half-written novel on a flash drive. Do I regret that I didn't complete it, that the world won't get to read it? Or regret instead the bank-holiday spent toiling on it in a darkened room while outside the sun was dancing and my lover lay waiting in the grass.

On the Line

Philippa Bowe

Today's a green day. It's alright to add a bit of turquoise, but that's as far as I'll go. The washing line flails with T-shirts, leggings, carefully twinned socks. A dress the colour of a kingfisher's wing. While I'm at it I'll add an aloe vera, a big bunch of mint and a parrot's feather. Just to be on the safe side.

I peg them and squint across the valley to the village. Where my dear progenitors dwell in their inappropriate house with its steep staircase and uneven floors. My colours pull them up out of the arms of their chairs and into the outside world, a healthful walk among oh-so-green trees and beneath an oh-so-blue sky.

On a red day (orange allowed), plenty of knickers, always more socks, too many T-shirts dammit, and just one saucy bra, next to a dangling string of shiny espelette peppers and netted pomegranate seeds. The Crumblies don't go out, stir up the fire in the kindly indoors, stay warm, bury their gaze in the blistering flames and watch the memories burn and disappear up the chimney in twists of smoke.

The only other day that counts is white. A waft of shirts and shirts and shirts, and then all the fine, wrinkled, blowing linen. Hardly room for more, just a few sheets of virgin paper. On a white day the old people lay themselves down in benign sheets for a loving nap, smiles on bedside-table dentures, translucent eyelids fluttering.

I can't wash the dark things. The dangers are much too real. I know them, they're lurking. Preying on brittle bones, shaky limbs. Treacherous tumbles on murky slick pavements. Plum-purple bruises. Black nightmares in the wee hours. The last time ended in a broken ankle for her and a nasty nearly-eye cut for him.

So the funeral garb and footwear, crow's foot and chip of volcanic stone are left to moulder in shadowy corners of my house. If I take them to the line, I know the siren will start screaming, ambulance lumber on its way, scooping up mother or father or both. And they'll take the colours with them as they go.

Houses

Grace Ridley

And I sat and I thought about how little people live in little houses and how big people live in little houses also. I thought about how little people live in big houses and how big people live in big houses too.

I thought about little people in little houses, with big ideas of how they belong in big houses and how big people in big houses have small ideas about small houses.

I thought about how we're all constantly moving around these big and small dwellings and whether (small or big) we ever make our way to the big houses of the small lodgers' dreams, and whether the big people in the big houses care when... or where... or why... or how... the small people move from their small houses.

And I was all at once sad. Thinking about the houses of the big and small people moving through their small and big lives. All of them wondering if, or why, the others should care.

I wonder ultimately are we all trapped?

Are we all just small and big people moving around small and big houses just desperately looking for the door?

Memorising the Future

Michelle Matheson

Her skin is a symphony of perfection.

I marvel at this creation of mine. There is not a blemish to be seen. Not a hair, spot or scar to mar her. Just golden hair and sun-kissed limbs. I absorb the sight of her as she stands unaware of my scrutiny in the bathroom light. The tan lines of her swimsuit clearly visible.

In her haste to immerse herself in the tub, she casts clothes to all four corners of the room. She is not concerned with closing the bathroom door, too busy with the prospect of bubbles.

She is intent only on her interior world. She has donned her snorkel and mask, a naked scuba diver. She tells me gleefully of the coral and multi-coloured fish that grace our bathroom. A plastic shark is recruited to be her nemesis. Her tale so vivid I can almost see them too.

As we wash her hair, the transition into a mermaid begins. The scent of coconut shampoo is fragrant in the air. She stretches out full length in the bath, her hair floating around her. She inhabits her role like the grandest of stage actresses.

I lower my head and kiss her gently on the shoulder. She tastes like hope, like the future. She smiles, but it doesn't shift her focus.

My fingertips ache to touch her. When she was new born her body was an extension of my own. I was free to trace every curve of her, from the crown of head to the smallest of toes; to linger in the dainty creases of knee and elbow. Now she is impatient with me if I try to hold her for too long.

She is in no hurry to dress, busy telling me about her day. I dry her and manoeuvre her into her pyjamas. I try to force the feel of flannelette through the pores of my skin, to burn the gentle curve of her muscles into the retinas of my eyes. I want to memorise every scent and sight and sound, before this moment too is gone.

Equilibrium

Johanna Robinson

There are eight in her team, nudging down this slim northern river, their expectations carefully weighted. Fish swerve between her knees. *That's no job for a Jessica*, a man once said, over seafood. So she told him, between cocktail sips, how bodies rot underwater, that flesh dissolves more slowly in saltwater than fresh. She explained what happens to eyeballs, where blood goes, why bodies rise, sink and separate.

After her first time, Jessica vomited for two days. Perhaps it was the Thames' rank glut of chemicals, or maybe it was what they found: bones, riddled skin, parts. The Thames became brackish around Battersea, marine at Gravesend, and it disturbed her to think of limbs divided between saltwater and fresh, a soul unreconciled.

She learned to tell dead from alive, human from eel. The eels had arrived as larvae in the nineteenth century, her trainer said, in water taken on as ships' ballast in India, China, Malaysia. These days, the creatures spiralled up and down the Thames estuary, as if they owned the waters, as if they always had.

Now, far from London, Jessica traces a river that rises and dries, narrows and floods. A river that during a storm licks at the cold underside of old stone bridges. A river that harbours no eels, no ancient ballast, just water that was once ice.

'I don't know how you do your job,' people say.

'Someone has to.' She keeps her sister from them. Hides how she recognises the eels of grief darting through every vein. How the not-knowing presses on the chest like the weight of water. How half a body, even just a piece, can be enough to release that foreign, occupying weight of ballast. How each day requires calibration. How the wail from a mother's mouth is one of combined thanks and devastation, a brackish force of despair so fresh and yet so old and salted that it flows from the core of time itself.

The river's shallow; her flippers skim the bed and algae drapes her shoulders. She hopes and fears they will find the girl. Hopes and fears they won't. This is all the balance she needs.

The Snowbird

Barclay Rafferty

Four people, two moggies, and one Labrador-cross lived here. Four people crammed into an Austin Metro for a jolly to the coast. One week later, four beachcombers, one Austin Metro, and one porcelain teapot returned.

Mum picked it out: *That'd look lovely in our kitchen, Nige.* Dad cradled it to the car, towelled it into the boot, kept it pride-of-place in the eighties, under the sink in the nineties; picked it up now and then, traced faint blue lines, chipped at its exoskeleton before stuffing it away again.

Until Mum ankled in sometime in the noughties, bone china and biscuity cut-outs rattling to arthritic beats. Dad squinted over her shoulder from the green split-leather chesterfield, told her he'd like to dine on catfish, watch some dusty old Western where the racist limps sunward. And Mum said, *We never did those things, Nigel, we're British.* But Rory wasn't there to diffuse, squirrel-cheeked from cola cubes. And I wasn't there to tell him to *Shut up, you little prat,* or else you'll be watching that tele through a slipper-sized crater.

The teapot left the building shortly afterwards — became a gaff for seashells; the ones we found in Salcombe, the ones we haggled for in Brum. I place them on the mantle, where ghost pixels of Dad hang, furrowing over a drum-smooth expanse, waiting for a ship that came in while he slept.

Rory's arranged for a removal van; I have no car. I trot the teapot past sunken trolleys till it tumbles. Its cutty shards slash me red. I salvage shells, head home again to clean up, hear my voice in the periwinkle: *Don't give me your bankcard, for fuck's sake, you've probably got piles.* Rory, the family invertebrate, whinges from the whelk: *No one would snog you, not even for a hundred quid — Up yours!*

False teeth chatter in the jug on the ledge. Outside, wind inflates a plastic bag on speckled branches. Beyond is gothic snowfall and lights from other homes. The gale twists, whisks like gingerbread, dances to piccolos, reed flutes. I howl in the bluster: *You can't catch me!* — I'm two bags, three trains, one bus, and a present, elsewhere.

After the Rain

Sarah McPherson

We raced in the garden, youth and passion spilling into laughter through long hot afternoons until the rain came fat and heavy and, fretful, they called us in.

'You'll catch your death.'

Rain brings back an image of you, like a photograph. Your smile, eyes fixed on mine, hair in dripping rats-tails as they towelled us off, scolding all the while.

In the dark of my bedroom, the patter of drops on the window grew to a roar. A rush of blood; a wave swelling, breaking, flooding the secret parts of me until all I could think of was you.

You didn't notice.

I watched you, smiled with you, lent you clothes, held your hair when you came home drunk or crying again over what some boy had done or said or not said.

I only cry in the rain, even now, raindrops and teardrops mixing on my upturned face.

You didn't see me.

'Isn't she lucky, to have a friend like you,' they said. 'Aren't you lucky.'

But you were never mine, except for those brief moments in the garden, before the rain.

Lost Language

Laura Blake

When my grandmother fled her country, she was told she could only bring what she could carry on her back. I can picture her, frantically sorting her possessions, while the captain shouted that he'd sail without her if she didn't make haste. What choice did she have but to give up her mother tongue? It was packed in a heavy trunk; a lifetime of experiences expressed in words. She had never considered leaving it behind, but in desperation she pushed it, grunting, into the sea, then climbed the ship's gangway in silence.

'It was too heavy to carry,' she told me. 'We had twelve different words for grief alone.'

The sailors took pity on her and taught her new words to replace the ones she had lost. They threaded compliments, like beads, around her neck; *pretty; young; good girl.*

And the strangers that inhabited the New World, they too were as charitable as the sailors, showering the near-silent girl with jagged-edged slurs that clung to her with spiny thorns.

Unwelcome. Unwanted. Inferior.

Others she found abandoned; the shivering *unloved*, the needy *lonesome*, that sat, quivering, in the palm of her hand. She gathered up all the words she could find and stored them carefully away, promising not to make the same mistake again.

'In my country,' she said, 'the mother tongue was passed from mother to daughter. It was a precious gift. You kept it safe.'

One day I saw two foreign words in the dusty window of a second-hand store. They looked water-damaged and faded, as though they hadn't been spoken aloud in a long time. I purchased them and hurried home to grandmother, dropping them softly in her lap.

'*Lost*,' she said, with tears in her eyes, holding the words close to her heart.

'And *found*.'